MA-KEE

THE
LIFE
AND
DEATH
OF A
MUSKELLUNGE

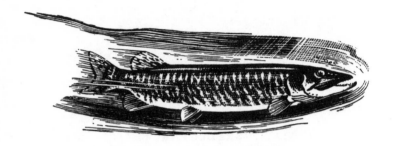

DAVID V. REDDICK

MA-KEE

THE LIFE AND DEATH
OF A MUSKELLUNGE

ILLUSTRATED BY GEOFFREY W. GOSS

MCCLELLAND AND STEWART LIMITED

Reprinted 1974

ALL RIGHTS RESERVED

The Canadian Publishers
McClelland and Stewart Limited
25 Hollinger Road, Toronto

0-7710-7414-X

Printed and bound in Canada

Contents

MA-KEE

THE
LIFE
AND
DEATH
OF A
MUSKELLUNGE

The Lakeland

IN all parts of the Lakeland, muskellunge were making their way to the creeks and marshes to spawn.

Under the pearly, wave-smoothed tree branch where she made her home, She, the big female, felt the impulse. During the winter she had idled the time away, choosing, save for occasional forages into deeper water, to stay close to the haunts she knew. But with the arrival of spring in the Lakeland she had grown restless.

She had never tried to understand the seasons, accommodating herself to them as conditions to be accepted and not questioned. Winter and summer, and their penumbral fringes, she roughly divided into the time of the shadow and the time of light.

The time of the shadow, when the chill bottom waters expanded and rose to form a steadily thickening ice skin, and layer upon layer of snow made a perpetual twilight below, was least to her liking. Then the larvae dug into the mud and were seen no more. Water boatmen and beetles sought the refuge of dark cavities in submerged root stalks. Minnows left the shore for the security of the depths. And even her beloved forests of hornwort and stately ruffle-leaf pondweed (the "coontail" and "muskie weed" of the angler) dwindled into nothingness.

At such times, life came to a standstill. And the shadow, the coarse night creature, settled its body over her domain.

But, ah! How different it was when the time of light

arrived. How different it had been since those moments of gradually lessening darkness when the night creature had shrieked and groaned and finally split asunder before a turbulence above, and allowed the welcome light to shed on her world once more.

From the time when the fierce March wind and persevering sun had set the lake free, the floodtide of life had begun. Little wonder that through the ensuing month, with the pitch of activity among the water creatures increasing day by day and upthrusting pondweeds contributing to the general atmosphere of rebirth, the strain of being a mere onlooker had become too much.

At first, She fed—on shiners, perch, leeches: any prey, large or small, that her sly pursuits and savage leaps would bring her. Then, the first rash of hunger diminished, she simply lay, ventral fins supporting her slightly inclined body like hands, content to draw within her the tumultuous excitement of it all, and to await the call of the marshes.

Now, that time has come. It is a day in early May. Already many of her kind have forsaken their hideouts for the marshes. Now She does likewise; and if nothing transpires to prevent her, she will return.

She is ten years old, and on a fisherman's scale would weigh twenty-one pounds. For six of her years she has made these annual trips to the spawning grounds, depositing in the process some two hundred thousand eggs. Possibly a thousand of these eggs have escaped the greedy mouths of shiners and sunfish and rock bass, with an even smaller number surviving the fourteen-day hatching period to face the dangers of life as fry and fingerlings. This year she will drop about seventy thousand eggs, of which no more than a dozen or so will develop into adult fish.

Easily She makes her way through deep water, skirting rocky points and stump-strewn inlets. The Great Marsh lies a mile in a straight line from her hideout, and she steers a course directly to it. To follow the shoreline, as she sometimes did when foraging, would take her three times as long.

Food she ignores. A sucker, rooting in the decayed bottom vegetation, scurries off under a protective cloud of silt as it is suddenly aware of her presence. Bass and dogfish respectfully give her a wide berth. But none are in danger.

She has not gone far when she is joined by a male muskellunge, and then immediately after, by another. They are both considerably smaller than She and take up positions for the rest of the trip one on either side of her tail.

Their satellite state is not to last long, however. In sight of the marsh, She passes close to a floating sedge-island, one of many that the winds have broken loose from the swamp shore to become temporary havens for any creatures that wish to escape the sun or lurk unseen while foraging.

A flash of silver, and from the shadow of the sedge-island she is joined by a third fish. It is a muskellunge almost as large as She herself. Viciously wheeling, the newcomer scatters the two satellites and, after making sure that they have been properly put to flight, swiftly takes up the position they have vacated.

During all this, She has betrayed no emotion. The process of acquiring a mate is one she has become used to and one in which she plays little part. It is usually, as now, the largest of her suitors that wins out. And if, when she is ready for courtship, there is still a persistent rival on the scene, she herself will turn and drive him off.

Cattails, not yet tinged with green above the water line, stand massed in thick, sere banks along the border of the marsh. In the brisk May wind they rattle blade against blade in a hollow clatter that is strangely at home with the plaintive *skree-skree* of the red-winged blackbirds that maintain precarious balance on the bending blades. From far back in the rush cover the white-beaked coot cackles giddily. A bittern, standing stiffly alert where the rushes end and the marsh grass begins, tries out the first of the season's fishing.

She is not the only one of her kind in the marsh that has found a mate. By now her successful suitor has moved up alongside her and they swim together as one fish. Other muskellunge are doing likewise, but none pay any attention to the others when in pairs. A lone male on occasion attempts to contest the ownership of a female, and there is a wild fierce circling by the males that sets the whirligig clusters scurrying and silts the water so that for a time it is difficult to see. Then the defeated fish goes its way and all is normal again.

For two days and nights She moves about the marsh with the male at her side.

On the morning of the day she is to spawn they lie quietly for a while in the open a foot or so under water.

A hundred feet overhead, Pandion, the osprey, circles the marsh. Newly returned from his winter haven in the Gulf of Mexico, a thousand miles to the south, Pandion had bent his initial efforts to repairing his last year's nest in the very topmost branches of a towering pine. Later, he will find a mate and, sometime in June, their shrill *pee-a pee-a* will sound faintly on the wind—his from high over the water, hers from the nest where her white under-feathers warm her brood.

But now he is interested only in food. Pandion's quarry is fish, a specialty that earned him the alternative name of fish hawk; and, in the taking of fish, he has no equal. Like the heron and the bittern, he takes his fish alive. And like them also, his best fishing is in the shallow shore waters and in the marshes. This is because his feathers are not oily. He cannot dive like the loon, and must rely on his powerful talons to clutch his quarry while his wings and body remain out of water.

His rapid plunge from dizzy heights is the core of his method of attack for there is almost no warning to the fish, so sudden is he upon it. And his keen eyes miss not even the glint of a chub despite the great heights from which he patrols.

From his station above the marsh Pandion has a clear view of the Lakeland. The Ojibway Indians, most powerful branch

of the great Chippewa nation, who had settled there following the defeat of the Hurons, gave to it the name Kawarthas,
meaning "Smiling Waters and Happy Land." They also re-
ferred to it as the meeting place of the lakes, for here the
seven lakes of the Kawarthas sat in everlasting council.

Sometimes when Mon-e-doo, the Great Spirit, became
angry, he caused the wind to lash the waters and give them
tongue so that they, together with the wind, might proclaim
his wrath. At such times their appearance was dark and for-
bidding. But now, in the pale morning sunlight, they glisten
like the scales of a huge fish—such a prize as Pandion, in
fancy born of hunger, might have taken and, with it in his
grasp, mounted to the skies.

Had the lakes indeed been scales and served as stepping
stones for a possessor of seven-league boots, forty miles would
have been taken up in a straight line from north to south
in crossing them. And yet, in the immensity of the country
in which they lie, they are as pools in a field after a rain.

In no special pattern they lie, nursed by the mother water
that flows through them and past them—a tenuous, placid
ribbon of river that most of the time loses its identity to the
larger lake expanses but which nevertheless is the artery that
connects them and gives them sustenance.

Trees crowd down to their very edges, and there stand
silently like a company of mourners—dark acres of pine and
balsam, mingled with the lighter greens of spruce and tamarack and, now and then, the maiden brightness of birch.
Wild rice and cattails are the dominant emergent plants of
their bays and shallow shores, while vast areas of stump-
strewn water tell of lands drowned as the result of artificial
flooding.

For there is more to this waterway than the chain of lakes
over which Pandion and others of his kind hold sway. Actually, it is a route from Lake Ontario to Georgian Bay on Lake
Huron, representing more than two hundred miles of canal-
linked river system, with the Lakeland lying almost precisely
in the middle.

The Trent Waterway, it is called, named for the wide deep valley of the Trent, ground out thousands of years before by a mighty post-glacial torrent and now providing the bed for the greater part of the system. Woodsmen had long used its flow to float logs to the mills. But this and the transporting of freight were dying enterprises, and the waters of the system, particularly the Lakeland, had become more familiar to the angler as the haunt of the bass and muskellunge, and to the holiday seeker who merely wanted the surcease from care that sun, wind and water would bring.

Circling, Pandion spies where She lies limned against the marsh ooze with her mate. It is a big prize, surely, but his wings are strong and he has hunger on his side to make them stronger. Once clutched fast in swift-piercing talons he can tear at eyes and soft understructure with his hooked beak. Victory could be but a matter of moments.

He gathers himself for the plunge. But stay—what manner of fish is his quarry? He drops lower for a closer look.

Now he is not so sure. The big grey fish looks larger, now, by far, than first glimpse had suggested. And the broad muscular back indicates power to be reckoned with. Even the smaller fish of the two looks quite a handful.

On the instant, Pandion changes his mind. Deep in his memory perhaps is the occasion when once before he had come to grips with a fish like these. He had been pulled half under water and barely got his claws free in time. And one other time when he was rising up with a sucker in his grasp, huge jaws snapped beneath him and a great grey body was gone with his prize.

His interest lost, the fish hawk soars to look for less formidable prey and is soon only a speck in the sky.

All unknowing, She continues to bask in the sun. In another hour she and her mate move into the rushes, where she deposits a stream of yellow eggs. They mound on the bottom and in the crevices between rush blades and stalks. Soon her partner's milky sperm cast a slow-settling mantle over the eggs—in veiling their gold fulfilling the promise of life to come.

The moon came out clear and silver that evening but set long before midnight. Hardly had it done so when a boat appeared silently out of the darkness of the shoreline and entered the Great Marsh.

In it were two men, one paddling slowly and with great caution, the other crouched on his knees in the bow. Over the side of the prow hung a coal-oil lantern, its glass polished to crystal clearness, its wick well trimmed, and the reservoir full. A whispered consultation took place and the man in the stern ceased paddling while his companion struck a match and, not without some difficulty, lit the lantern.

Now, with the yellow light throwing a ghostly patch on the water, the man in the prow reaches behind him and from the canoe bottom picks up a spear. It is a wide five-tined affair with a rough-hewn but tight-fitting hickory handle about four feet in length. This he grasps in one hand, holding it poised in a semi-ready position just above the surface of the water. Then he gives the signal to move on.

They are poachers. Barney, the man in the stern, is a farmer; Red, a loader at the sawmill near the village. It is not the first time they have speared fish and it will not be the last. They have discussed the expedition for days, knowing that the muskellunge are in the marsh and that the time for some rare sport has come.

In the late fall they will visit other lakes to spear white-fish, but it is a cold task and the fish run smaller. A half-dozen spawning muskies will keep their larders filled and their families fed for days. Their depredations bother Barney and Red not at all, for they are far from being alone in the practice. Some they know in the village who openly shoot the big fish with rifles in the daytime as the fish lie in the rushes. If the warden takes no note of such goings-on, what compunctions need they feel over some relatively innocent spearing by night?

A perch, robust with much feeding, first feels the bite of the tines but manages to scurry free with only the loss of a few scales to mark the encounter. It was hardly worth bothering about, other than to provide practice for the spear-wielder. Twenty feet farther on a better prize comes into view: a catfish of two pounds or so.

This time Red is successful. Levering the whiskery fish off against the thwart, like hay from a fork, he laughs in high good humour. Now, he tells Barney, his sights are sharp. It will be too bad for the first muskie he sees, large or small. Why, after that perch, which escaped only because he struck near the tail and the tines passed around instead of through it, he'll take the first muskie with his eyes closed.

She, the weight of spawn gone from her vitals, has fed

heavily in what remained of the day and now rests at ease, half in the open, half in a clump of rotted water plantains.

The light approaches, preceded by eerie, flickering shadows, at length discovering her and revealing the grim crocodile head and broad back . . . an easy target.

Swiftly Red thrusts the spear. There is a moment of pain as the steel skewers her flesh, then terror. She tries to run but cannot. Her tail whips the plantains into shreds. A storm of bottom muck and vegetation swirls about spear and fish. Waves, set up by the commotion, rock the canoe, and Barney, paddle thrust into the ooze, finds it is all he can do to hold the boat steady.

In a frenzy, She summons all her power and manages to squirm ahead a few feet, but boat and spearman move with her. The human muscles that have wrestled logs all winter are more than a match for her mightiest efforts and soon it is all over. Her strength ebbs and Red lifts her limp into the boat.

A fine fish—no doubt about that. They hold up the lantern to admire her and then quickly proceed with their work. For there is an hour's effort still ahead, and more and larger fish to be taken before they are satisfied. Besides, they are chagrined to find that their prize has spawned. It means that many of their quarry have probably quit the marsh.

On the canoe bottom, She lives out the last moments of her life in the matter-of-course way that has characterized her affairs since birth. Death had always been close. Now that it had struck, it did little more than chill her.

Short hours before, she had played her part in helping to stem the tide that was running ever faster against her kind. Now only death and defeat are reflected in her gaunt features and staring eyes.

In the Great Marsh

TWO large golden shiners were waiting to feed on the eggs before She had finished dropping them. Soon they were joined by a tribe of blunt-nosed minnows which assisted in devouring most of the spawn that was readily available and would have gone to greater trouble had not the sudden appearance of a high-backed perch put them to flight.

When the perch was gone, and the shiners had had their fill, there was little left. Fortunately, a few eggs had been overlooked. One of these owed its salvation to the marauders themselves for it had been whisked by their movements into a clump of water-lily roots. There it lay safely for fourteen days while the sun warmed it through and it developed eyes and mouth and fins and at length became recognizable as a fish.

Even then, the little muskellunge did not move about much. The egg sac with which she was saddled acted like an anchor, limiting her to short, balloon-like flights. And this was just as well. For danger was all about her, and she was easy prey. Besides, the quest for food was the chief reason for activity in this water world and, for the time being at least, this was a requirement that need not concern her. Well stocked with yolk, her egg sac could provide her with ample nourishment until she was able to feed for herself.

Hardly yet conscious of the momentous fact of being alive, the days passed quickly for the young muskellunge. Life, while she remained in this transitory state, part fish, part egg, consisted merely of existing. There was no honour in the clumsy guise in which she was cast; no glory in the existence that confined her to an area of bottom muck hardly larger than that which a sunfish could cross with a single stroke of its fins.

True, her small body was gradually taking shape. But she was still semi-transparent, and her flesh had not firmed into the hard, rapier lines characteristic of her kind. In clear light, when there was no wind to agitate the water and make it cloudy with silt and bits of vegetation, her entire arterial system stood out in sharp relief as though she had swallowed some drifting water plant, and its fine tracery of stem and branches had remained miraculously preserved within her.

She was even blind to her environment, seeing but not retaining, conscious only of a suddenly realized need to open and close her mouth as often as she could, and to give sporadic thrusts with her fins. The action of opening her mouth caused her to draw in water, as a land creature would take in air. This, in turn, impelled her to use her gills, for unless she ejected the water she would drown.

So simple a matter as breathing was easily learned. And the blood cells in her gills that extracted the life-giving oxygen did so without force of concentration on her part. Poor, insignificant creature: fourteen days she had spent on the marsh bottom as a helpless globule of no more consequence than the smallest struggling amoeba; fourteen days from the moment when a single successful male sperm had fought its way into the egg dropped by She, the great female muskie, and produced fertilization, until the day when the egg had shown unmistakable signs of becoming a fish. And now, days afterward, the little muskellunge was still in the throes of arriving at her true self.

Compared with the egg-saddled muskellunge, a mosquito larva was a superior being. For, while the little wrigglers took longer to hatch, here they were already in the marsh in their teeming thousands, swimming, breathing, feeding, leading a full and complete intermediate existence. And they were yet to know existences as pupae and imagos, whereas the young muskellunge was restricted to the single metamorphosis from egg to fish. So favoured also were the beetles and caddis flies that frequented the marsh, while such other insects as stone-flies, mayflies, and dragonflies, which somehow were cheated of the glories of the pupal stage, were only one step less well off.

But the plight of the young muskellunge was not to last much longer. When she was three weeks old she had completely absorbed her egg sac. She was now a fish in all truth. What is more, she was now ready to commence foraging, and the creatures of the marsh had best watch out.

Ma-Kee's initial forays were spiced with the delights of experimentation. Food was everywhere and in infinite variety in the Great Marsh for even such a tiny being as she. And there would be food aplenty for her later on, no matter how big she might become, providing no untoward circumstances arose to upset the balance of life as it existed in the marsh, and in the lake and river system of which the marsh was a part.

It had as its nucleus the multitude of plant and animal organisms that drifted in the surface waters of the marsh like pollen in the atmosphere. This was the plankton population, an almost invisible blanket of living things, through which the sun could easily shine, yet without which the entire chain of aquatic life would perish.

Themselves depending only on the free elements in the water set loose by light and warmth—the dissolved gases and raw materials of foods—these organisms were fed upon ravenously by swarms of minute crustaceans which, in turn, became food for young fish. Larger fish had the smaller fish to prey on and, in addition, a rich assortment of insect larvae, frogs, leeches and other creatures, all of which fed on the lesser plankton-eating animals or on plankton itself.

This intricate framework of existence did not end there. The fine balance, with its remote poles of sun and water, depended on other things for its maintenance. The larger water plants, for instance. These, too, contributed to the rhythm of life by providing food and protection to multitudes of plant-feeding insects and larvae, and by giving off oxygen to add to the never-too-plentiful store absorbed by the water from the air above.

Large fish used the weed beds as cover, hopeful of passing prey. Schools of catfish lolled in the shade of lily-pad clusters during bright summer afternoons, occasionally nosing off water mites and midge larvae that fed on the viscid algae masses on the underside of the pads and on the stems. Mayfly larvae, earlier, had fed on the decayed bottom vegetation, while dragonfly nymphs and water scorpions stood by, waiting to catch the timid plant-eaters in rapacious jaws.

Every single thing indeed, here in the Great Marsh, is of strategic value in fulfilling the daily pattern of living. All that depend on it are threatened should any part of the structure go awry.

And now, with a healthy environment favouring her, comes the young muskellunge to commence life at the very bottom of the structure. So perfectly arranged is it, it might have been made to her order.

The dainty, shrimp-like scuds that streaked like shooting stars through the watery firmament, and the restless nebular formations of cladocerans, first roused her appetite. But the scuds were too big a mouthful for her. And so, after failure here, she turned her attention to the busy cladocerans.

These diminutive creatures, some of them no bigger than a grain of sand, proved elusive targets. It was not just a matter, she soon found, of charging in amongst them and gobbling them up as fast as she could open and close her jaws. Her blind rushes only caused them to scatter, and she was fortunate if a single one rewarded her efforts. Thwarted, she would wait until they had reassembled. Then she would blunder in again, with the same results.

Hunger drove her to try new tactics. Before long she discovered that, by moving ever so cautiously, she could get close enough to actually lie among them. There she would go ignored, for the water fleas recognized danger only in movement, responding collectively to the slightest disturbance as though they were a single being.

In the thick of the swarming creatures she lay like a piece of reed, darting forward every now and again to seize one. When she could, she would take several in her mouth and retire to the protection of the sedge grass to consume them at her ease.

This was Ma-Kee's first lesson in patience. As time went on, the ability to withstand the temptation of food until it was almost within her grasp was to govern her entire existence.

Plankton crustacea, too, formed part of her diet at this stage. The largest of these minute animal entities she could snap up singly. But for the most part she simply cruised about, letting them flow into her open mouth and filtering out the water with her gills. The resultant collection of organisms, while never great, helped to assuage her hunger and provide her with the variety of nourishment she required.

As she grew, she sought bigger and bigger prey. The scuds she soon attacked without a tremor, waiting until their acrobatic flights brought them within range, for they were difficult to catch otherwise. One day a fearsome, many-legged sow bug clambered across the bottom almost underneath where she lay in wait by the rush fringe. Startled, she seized the unfortunate insect and began the pleasurable task of swallowing it. Yet, scant weeks before, the appearance of the same sow bug would have caused her to retreat in uncertainty.

The young muskellunge was progressing. With each new conquest she acquired additional confidence. But she had not yet learned the meaning of danger.

By now it is early summer. About the marsh there is the freshness and colour of plant life emerging into full bloom. In the choked profusion of growing things the marsh grasses dominate, rising up unchallenged in thick shining acres from marsh edge to distant field. Here and there a glimpse of shy yellow tells of marigolds that have also taken root in the spongy bog-ground that nurtures the grasses, while in the marginal waters of the marsh itself the narcissus-like flowers of the arrowheads blossom serene amid protecting armies of sharp-pointed bur reeds.

The sun, high in the ecliptic, sends down a clear, sparkling light that reveals neglected facets of beauty in leaf and stalk and flower, burnishing rush spears as though with cloth and wax, sharply distinguishing each tough or fragile thing that Nature has seen fit to summon into being. Swift dancing fires rain incessantly on the water surface, giving to it a gaiety and animation in keeping with the surge of life everywhere around. Even the air seems alive with an understanding of the new season.

Out beyond the rush fringe the broad leaves of spatterdock and castalia—the yellow and the white water lilies—after weeks of striving have finally pushed their way to the surface where they will make fine lounging platforms for frogs, stepping stones for coots and gallinules, and temporary resting places for terns and other small water birds. In the openings between the rush stalks appear lacy mats of green. This is the duckweed, a deceptive collection of floating plants with slender, hair-like roots, no one of which is larger than a perch scale, yet which, pushing one against the other and becoming overlapped and entwined, give the impression of a continuous blanket of surface vegetation. Where the water deepens and the potamogetons flourish, stiff spikes of mare's-tail protrude from the surface: appropriate mooring posts for the damselflies that will soon leave their nymphal cases and take to the air.

In tune with all this is the ceaseless movement and chatter of bird life; the busy, soundless activity of the marsh insects.

Under the surface of the marsh there is the same luxurious growth, making up in variegated greens and yellows what is lacking in floral decoration. Streamers of wild celery contrast their slender blades with thick chain-like clumps of elodea. Vivid patches of luminous green mark the water mosses where they have taken hold at random on the shallow bottom and on submerged logs. And the ceaseless goings and comings of the myriad underwater creatures produce an even greater tempo of activity than the life above.

Surely, nowhere in all creation is there a place more passionately, more fittingly, concerned with the occupation of existing than here in the Great Marsh.

Out by the ragged rim of bur reeds on this summer day, floating midway in the water above the marsh bottom, a monster lurks. Against the background of slender plants, the monster appears huge. Its grim-visaged head is like some prehistoric saurian's; its eyes as baleful as a crocodile's. A passing minnow suddenly brings the monster into focus and reveals it as none other than the young muskellunge. But Ma-Kee, to the tiny creatures upon which she preys, must *seem* a monster.

From time to time, as the breeze bends the reeds and shadows pass over her body, she loses identity altogether. But when the reeds are still, and the sunlight illumines her from head to tail, each detail of her appearance is clearly seen.

She is long and slender: as perfectly shaped as though moulded with infinite patience from some bright metal. The silver undercoating of her body is broken up by dark stripes that run vertically from back to flank, giving her a tigerish appearance. Even her fins and tail carry a hint of these markings to complete a disguise well suited to her shadowy haunts.

And if her body has a tigerish look, her resemblance to four-footed predators does not end there. For her sunken, slightly shovel-shaped head and tapering snout suggest more the fox. Here is a hint of the sagacious cunning with which her kind is endowed. And the deep, grim line of her jaws and the flat, malicious eyes set high on her head seem like physical manifestations of the savage ferocity that will characterize her actions in the life-and-death struggle that lies ahead of her.

In all the marsh there is no more deadly engine of destruction. Yet she measures hardly more than an inch in length.

A quick movement that causes the black, powdery mud of the bottom to rise like a column of smoke, and the young muskellunge has taken a water bug. Hardly has she regained her position than there is a disturbance from behind.

It is a bittern, fishing the shallow shore waters. Soon it will find a place in the reeds where the water is open and there it will stand patiently, its brownish body and striped yellow neck lost in the confusion of marsh growth, its long beak cocked upward at an angle like the tapering point of a rush spear, while it keeps watch for frogs, minnows, and the like. But now it is in motion and though it proceeds with measured tread, setting each foot down with the greatest care, the bending reeds give warning of its coming.

With a lightning thrust of her fins Ma-Kee is gone, braking to a stop several feet away. Only mildly alarmed, her momentary halt gives her a chance to size up the situation, for she is not sure what it is that has disturbed her.

Then, terror!

The bittern, spying her flight, has pursued her, and with the rapidity of an arrow thrusts its beak downward in her direction. Ma-Kee feels the surge of water as the bittern's head breaks the surface. And there is the distinct sound of the great beak snapping, right at her very tail.

Stricken with fear, blinded by mud and bits of vegetation, she darts aimlessly in several directions. Then, finding herself in clear water again, she swims furiously ahead until, quite by accident, she arrives at a wide creek that feeds the lower end of the marsh.

Not until she is far up the creek does she pause. But her safety is only momentary. Two boys are on the bank of the creek: Blackie, tall and dark-countenanced, and Bert, his friend. With them they have a small seine net, with which they hope to capture enough minnows to go perch fishing. They know the creek well, having seined it many times before. And now, each with his trousers rolled as high up around the thighs as he can manage, they step gingerly to the side of the creek.

Behind them on the bank is a pail half-filled with water to receive the minnows once the net is dragged ashore. The net, a very efficient instrument, with lead weights to help it hug the bottom and wood blocks to keep the top at water level, is almost certain to produce results. At each end, at the bottom, the stout cord on which the net is strung is tied in a loop. Each boy passes a loop around one bare foot—the closest to the net—then grasps the long upper line that will give them full control of the net as they move through the water. These young fishermen are masters of their craft.

With the net parallel to the bank, Blackie wades in cautiously, moving the foot with the loop in a shuffling motion over the bottom as he proceeds. When all is right, he will swing the net in a wide circle, Bert moving at a slower pace along the water edge until, pausing, the signal is given to bring the far end of the net to shore.

In the water, directly in the area to be netted, Ma-Kee at once perceives this new danger and rushes from the silt clouds that forecast it. But Bert has equipped himself with stones, which he tosses one at a time into the water as he moves up the bank—an effective way of turning fleeing minnows back into the circle of the net.

Danger from behind, and now from in front. The gurgling, chugging sound of the stones and the huge silvery paths they make as they sink to the bottom send new fear into the young muskellunge.

Turning, uncertain, she rushes toward the far bank which so far has been free of disturbance. Too late. The net is now being drawn and she is in the middle, together with a throng of agitated sand minnows.

"They're in! They're in!" the boys exult, at the precise moment lifting the net with its mass of tumbling silver. It is exciting, this minnow netting. Almost as exciting as the fishing that will follow. Blackie who, because of his long legs, has made the sweep, is not even aware that his pant leg has slipped down and is wringing wet. Of what consequence such mishaps when youth and adventure go hand in hand midst carefree summer days?

In a rush, the boys swing the net onto the bank and lay it open. On hands and knees they begin to scoop up the minnows and deposit them in the pail. Soon the job is done. It is a fine haul and they begin to lift the net to give it a rinsing, for they will not need it again that day.

But a last-minute inspection reveals a small dark-barred fish, its gill-covers caught in a torn place in the net where it has almost made its way through.

"Look!" Bert exclaims delightedly, extricating the fish and holding it up to view in his cupped hand. "A little muskie! Shall we try him?"

"Naw!" Blackie shows his disgust at the suggestion. "Ever hear of a perch taking a muskie? Most likely'd run for it. Even from a baby like this."

"But what'll we do with him?"

"Oh, toss him back." Blackie has a sudden heartening thought. "Who knows? Maybe he'll grow up to be a big one —forty or fifty pounds, even. And we'll catch him again. Not in a net, though."

He tosses Ma-Kee back into the creek. For a while she lies on her side recovering from the effects of the harsh dry element into which she had been precipitated. Then, slowly, she comes upright and works her way to the bottom.

Luck had been with her. She will not always be so fortunate.

Water Tiger

MA-KEE did not return to the marsh that day, nor for several days.

While she recovered from her faintness, she lay on the sandy creek bottom, half in, half out of a tuft of weed, caring little whether she was properly hidden. Later, when her energy had returned, she swam slowly to the nearest reed patch where a canopy of floating frog spittle provided a shadowy retreat. There she rested, content to look out over the undulating plane of the creek bed and take note of her new environment.

Life was not as abundant in the creek as in the marsh. There was a noticeable scarcity of familiar water bugs such as fairy shrimps and scuds and boatmen—a lack related to the similar shortage of water plants and the absence of the thick muck floor that breeds larvae as gelatin breeds bacteria. Even the ubiquitous cloud-layers of algae and desmids were less concentrated. And, try as she would, the young muskellunge spied out not a single swirling bundle of cladocerans.

Nevertheless, there was no lack of activity. For the creek was the home of many sunfish, their quick agitated movements making the sunlit shallows alive with colour. And every so often schools of sand minnows moved in leisurely fashion through the quiet water like sightseers. There were many other signs as well to indicate that here was no empty, lifeless world: the sinuous ribbony passage of a horse leech which, alarmed by the shadow of a flitting wagtail, suddenly became a frozen brown ball clutched to a stone; gravity-defying mosquito wrigglers bent on spending recuperating moments with their breathing tubes thrust upwards through the water skin; the jewel flash of a dace that, bursting from the cover of a frail weed, abruptly terminated one wriggler's journeying.

There was life, indeed, in this pulseless vein of water. But the young muskellunge could not see all. Above and beyond, there were still other things to exclaim that here in this wooded area, watered but sparingly, yet in daily communion with sun and air, Nature had not passed by without allocating living space for many of the creatures in her care.

The creek, in reality, owed its existence to the backed-up water of the lake. Rivulets from the woods fed it and helped to keep it fresh. But as the summer advanced and the level of the Lakeland waters fell, it would partially dry up and most of its inhabitants would depart or fall victim to the drought.

Not a great distance from its banks small poplars stood gracefully erect amid closely encroaching shrubs. Behind them, in places where the land was lower, willows thrived. And then the cedars took over in formidable frowning ranks, thronging the lanes beside the creek until before long the latter dissipated into spongy bog-ground. After that, the fields began, merging into the gentle hills that overlooked much of the Lakeland.

Between the trees and the creek, coarse spikes of yellow dock summon the cabbage butterfly, and milkweed pods stand stiff and unopened, veiling in harsh green the wonder of the silken seed-flower within. August would see the pods broken; in September, Boreas would spend many a boisterous hour whisking the seed parachutes aloft in cushioned flight to alight where chance dictated. September, too, would see the goldenrod abloom, and the fading glory of the evening primrose.

Thick grass clumps make a clumsy carpet from which all else protrudes. Passage along either lane beside the creek is further impeded by rotted logs and by indentations where reed clusters encroach upon the land as though discontented with their usual marginal existence. With the onset of the dry season, however, the invasion would be thwarted.

Cattle and two-legged creatures would experience difficulty in negotiating this stretch, but other inhabitants do not. The minx-eyed deer mouse manages any obstruction in a scamper. And now, the water wagtail that frightened the leech carries on his bustling agitated search for grubs in the very thickest part of the tangle.

How piercing sweet his liquid song, as, for a moment, he clings to bending reed and tilts his pert striped head skywards. With the strenuous *che-wee* of the yellow warbler that has ventured out from his home in the dogwoods he adds lofty emphasis to what the eye knows full well: that this is truly the high tide of the year and that whatever of life ebbed away short months before is now returned in full flood.

Where the creek narrows and its feeble remnant spreads into wide flat puddles that by degrees are blotted up by the low bog-ground, a regular hatchery is in operation.

Here, differing from the sandy area where Ma-Kee rests beneath her canopy of filamentous algae, are ideal conditions for the propagating and nurturing of the larval stages of aquatic insects. The mayflies, in particular, have found it to their liking, and each year for many years they have dropped their eggs on the still water of the pools. And each year for many years larvae have hatched and crawled about, dug into the mud as winter approached, reappeared in the spring, and eventually, as sub-imagos, have flown to overhanging trees and shrubbery to shed their confining shells and come forth as shining winged imagos to commence the process all over again.

For days now, in the early evening, new hatches have participated in the rhythmic rising, falling, wedding flights: ephemeral, ecstatic excursions into the blue, that have ended in sudden death when their procreational functions were fulfilled. In another day or two the last of the hatches will have taken wing and the mayfly season will be over.

Dragonfly larvae also lurk in these sun-warmed shallows, for what more appetizing feast could they find than the juicy mayfly nymphs and sub-imagos? Keeping them savage company are the water scorpions, which await their prey from upside-down positions on reed and rush stalks, and adult water bugs, which depend on water tension to maintain them when feeding, also in a head-down position.

Fiercest predator of all is the larva of Dytiscus, the diving beetle. In its long narrow body with its segmented back-plates, six powerful legs, and cruel sickle-shaped jaws, is compacted the very substance of voraciousness.

It is the water tiger. What being, scaled to this miniature water world, would not quail before the sight of this rearing monster, rising up out of the dead bottom like an apparition to put a sudden end to whatever it confronted?

Dytiscus has fed, this day, to the full. And now, in the drowsy afternoon, has succumbed to lethargy. In the evening it will be time to begin again.

It is late June. The spawning ceremonies of the sunfish are under way.

From her hideout, Ma-Kee watches an orange-chested pouter pigeon of a male attempting to entice a female into the shallow depression he has whisked out with tail and fins in the sand near the bank. A handsome fellow, this, with his high-arched blue-green back and freckled green and yellow sides.

The less eloquently coloured female hovers hesitantly just outside the nest. When he preens himself and spreads open the translucent, many-rayed fan that characterizes the sunfish family, she is carried away altogether.

Now she joins him, and together they circle round and round in the nest. Gay, valiant little fish: how fortunate they cannot envision what perils yet await their lives. Overhead on a dead tree limb perches Halcyon the kingfisher. There will come a day when desperation will drive him to tackle even so chunky and well-armed a prize. In the marsh, when

the sunfish population has retreated there during the August
drought, Chelydra, the snapping turtle, with jack-in-the-box
head and horny beak, will lie waiting, her moss-backed shell
half covered in the mud bottom. And out on the sand flats of
the lake shoreline, on the fringe of the oval-leaved potamogetons, should they venture that far, is Ravenor, of the
spike-toothed head and black shark-like body.

The sunfish do not know and they do not care. Life, for
them, is for the moment. For an hour or more they circle,
sometimes leaving the nest to scurry wildly through the thin
vegetation, always side by side. Presently, ventral surfaces
touching, spawn and milt are extruded in unison. When the
event is over, the female departs, leaving the male the task
of defending the egg-litter from the sand minnows which,
by sight or scent, have been attracted to the scene.

Ma-Kee, momentarily arrested by the event, is aware now
of another sensation. The shadow beneath her canopy is
deepening. She has not fed since morning and there is little
left of the day. Her stomach is not to be denied.

Back to the marsh? No, she is not yet keen on that. And so,
slipping easily out into mid water, she makes her way towards the creek end.

Dytiscus has roused from his stupor by the time Ma-Kee
arrives.

The air is filled with emerging mayflies. The reeds are a
veritable graveyard of nymphal skins. Overhead, in a silent
paean to approaching twilight, the dancing flight has begun.
Swarms of mayfly spinners, using tree limbs as initial spring-
boards, mount higher and higher, their diaphanous wings
shedding light like flakes of crystal. And now down again,
tail ruddering the swift descent, until the lesser ranks of the
females are reached. Then up again. Over and over.

Spent flies are falling to the ground and to the water surface. But not all these slender-bodied creatures taste death
naturally, nor enjoy the full period of the mating flight. For,
long before, a redstart has come to the creek, hovering on the
edge of the swarm, darting in now and again to seize a flying

insect, operating its slender beak-trap as fast as dainty prey can be stuffed into over-choked crop.

Two white circles, fastened to two wing shadows, the whole diving and turning in bat-like manoeuvres, now are thrust into the aerial scene. The nighthawk is here, adding his mastery to the onslaught.

The mayflies are having an equally hard time of it in the pool. Ma-Kee has arrived and is stuffing herself with every nymph within reach that does not manage to escape her by chance metamorphosis to winged insect.

Dytiscus, too, is at work.

In the west, the sky is afire with oriflamme hues that throw their resemblance upon the surface of the pool. Trees and bushes stand out in stiff relief like stage scenery.

Gradually the fire smoulders. In its wake come soft undertones of colour that spread across the horizon as though oil were being poured on a vast yellow sea. These are soon gone, to leave only the sea of ochre. The yellow fades to white, tinged with silver. Shadows all at once deepen to join the mysterious blackness of advancing night.

As with the quenching of a brilliant flame, and the lighting of a candle, twilight has descended.

Under water, things are still quite visible, and will continue to be throughout the night if the sky remains cloudless. Ma-Kee, moving but a short distance from the scene of her depredations, allows herself to sink to the bottom, ready to rest the night and digest the contents of her craw. On the instant of touching the bottom she becomes aware of the looming form of Dytiscus—but too late to avoid the pincer-like jaws that fasten on her.

Again terror. Swift, unreasoning terror. Twice before in one day she has known it. Only for an instant does it rob her of her energy. Then she is off through the water in a frenzy, towing Dytiscus after her.

The water tiger has a hold near her tail. Had it known what manner of fish it had seized, it might not have been so eager. For, in her wild dash, the young muskellunge whips her tail from side to side, flinging her attacker against water plants and other obstructions.

The battle, however, is one-sided. The water tiger is three inches long—fully an inch longer than Ma-Kee. And though its jaws cannot quite pierce the scale-covering on Ma-Kee's sides, it shows no signs of relaxing its hold. It is not the first time it has attacked a fish and always it has emerged victorious. Several times its victims have been larger than Ma-Kee. But usually they were sand minnows or dace, and in this victim it finds unexpected strength.

Soon Ma-Kee slows her pace. The weight is too much for her.

Now she stops altogether, feeling light-headed. She cannot get enough oxygen, and she gulps in water in an almost continuous flow. If only she can rest long enough she may be able to twist about and turn the tables by seizing her attacker. But, at the moment, this is quite beyond her.

Dytiscus, for the first time, is able to secure a better hold. At the same time it straddles Ma-Kee, hooking each of its sharp-toed legs firmly to her sides.

It is too late now for her to launch a counter-attack. Her only hope is to dislodge the grotesque creature with the saucer eyes and segmented dragon-like body that is like an Old Man of the Sea upon her back.

Once more she tows her attacker, this time away from the deeper part of the creek. Although she swims high in the water, her underside presently touches bottom and she is back at the mayfly hatchery.

Her senses are confused. She has lost control of her body and she lists slightly like an overloaded ship.

But suddenly, inexplicably, the weight on her back decreases. Dimly she senses another struggle going on above her, in which her adversary is an unwilling combatant. In another moment, the pincers which have set up a gnawing ache back of her dorsal are released; then the legs.

She is free! A piece of good fortune had sent her under the spot where a giant water beetle—ironically enough, a close relation of Dytiscus—hung suspended, head down, from the surface film. A prone target having thus been delivered to the beetle, it had lost no time in seizing upon the opportunity.

But the little muskellunge was in no condition to receive satisfaction from sight of her attacker being torn apart—had she been inclined to stay and watch.

The mud bottom among the reeds soothed her, as did the mucous algae coating on the plant stems, against which she rubbed.

After a few days the soreness left her. No serious damage had been done. But she felt it high time to return to the marsh.

Under a sky the colour of grey milk, fitful wind gusts spring from nowhere to race across the water, giving it a nutmeg-grater appearance. The air has a moist coolness, welcome after days of heat. The fish hawk is aloft, and over the wind-buffeted landscape there is a sense of restlessness.

Now, faint dangling legs of rain-laden cloud begin to form. Noting this, the marsh wren, which has been busily hunting insects from its lily-pad landing base, returns to its nest amid the rushes, for experience tells it that hunting will soon be fruitless. Already, anticipating the rain, the majority of flies and midges have taken cover in emergent vegetation at hand.

Below, poised expectant at the edge of a bladderwort forest, Ma-Kee senses the feeling of depression that the change in atmospheric pressure has brought about. As a rule, this would render her temporarily inactive. But she has fed only sparingly since her return to the marsh. The driving force of hunger is upon her. And so, she is ready to forage regardless.

Besides, her keen hearing, aided by the almost invisible lateral line that runs horizontally along both sides of her body and by means of which she is able to perceive low-frequency vibrations, has conveyed to her the sounds of a commotion from out in the marsh.

A damsel fly is struggling in the water where it has been

blown by the treacherous wind. Each gust sends it scudding across the surface, feebly fluttering. It has been seen first by a school of whirligigs, but they dare not venture so far from the security of the reed clusters. The marsh wren is now departed and it, too, is cheated of an easy catch.

What, then, are the coruscated movements in the area of the hapless insect? What pulls off first one leg and then another? What tiny red mouths collectively tear at the damsel fly's amethyst-blue abdominal structure?

Several shiners have discovered the flotsam and converge on it as unexpected booty. They are plump little fellows, with black stripes running from tail to chin. When they turn, they reveal an iridescent colouring that is sometimes pink, sometimes blue. All in all, they are as inviting to look at in their eager, flashing movements as the creature with whom they are playing tug-of-war.

Nearer and nearer to Ma-Kee they come. Now they are almost overhead, and the young muskellunge feels a kind of trembling mounting within her.

So far, her diet has been limited to the insect life of the marsh, and to plankton. But of late she has felt increasingly dissatisfied with such fare. Food is a dominant need, and it takes more and more to fill her craw. Now, here is prey to match her craving.

As she has grown, she has moved inexorably closer to this moment. It is an important stage in her career. To meet and dispatch such quarry, to match cunning with cunning, speed with speed, will alone prove her fitness as a member of a great predator species.

Food: the demand overwhelms her. Her stomach must be filled with something big enough to satisfy its capacity.

The nearest shiner sees her, but is not alarmed, for it is only slightly smaller than Ma-Kee. Tensely, the young muskellunge gathers herself for the leap. Her tail lowers and her back hunches. Now. . . .

The bold leap is successful. Ma-Kee's jaws close on the tender body. Roseate scales, shaken loose in the ensuing struggle, descend in a glittering shower to the bottom. But it is soon over, for the shiner is a forage fish and its strength ebbs quickly.

Glutton-like, the young muskellunge retires to the bladder-wort cover to gorge her prey. She can get it only halfway down, and a day elapses before the half-digested front end reduces in size to a point where the whole fish can be engulfed.

It is a fine meal, a filling meal: the first meal wholly appropriate to her predatory role.

Shore Refuge

THE days pass and it is August. The marsh now begins to take on a sere look—the withering influence of sun and drought. Inshore, many plants that once enjoyed the moist touch of water about their roots now rear nakedly from harsh, cracked ground. Above the water line, the heavy rush banks that hug the uneven circle of the marsh, in and out, like green-slimed moat-walls, are stained yellow to the height of a foot, telling how far the lake level has dropped.

In the creek it is a similar story, only a more tragic one. The mayfly pools are reduced to sodden bog; the creek itself to half its former width. Gone are the sunfish. Gone, save for a few venturesome specimens, are the minnows. It is a place now only for those surface-dimpling gadabouts of the quiet reaches, the water striders, and goggle-eyed leopard frogs and toads.

But as if to compensate for the setbacks it has suffered, the marsh country has achieved a thousand new wonders. Castalia, the pond lily, is in bloom, and on the choked surface of the marsh a throng of satiny-white heads sit, as if guillotined, on flat green pillows. Coarser, heavy-petalled spatter-dock blooms are sun-filled goblets stained with red. And as though dropped from the bosom of the night, a regular milky way of star flowers lights up the surface.

On land, the bold-flowering trumpet weed attracts colourfully garmented butterflies. Now comes the dragonfly on shimmering wings, circling the marsh in stiff arrow-flight.

He has caught a gnat in mid air and pauses on a lily-pad to devour it. Presently, like a watchman on his rounds, he will take to the air again, continuing his hunting flights periodically until dusk.

Ma-Kee, meanwhile, knows nothing of the oppression of the waning season, or of its altered guise. She knows only that down in her sea-green world there is food in abundance. And, to her, that is all that matters.

She now feeds largely on minnows. She is a wraith that haunts the weed beds and the shadowy places by the lily-pad stalks, creating terror with her sudden appearance, wreaking havoc with the savagery of her onslaught.

The great flocks are at her mercy. It is a game; a savage, one-sided game, with the minnows inevitably the losers.

She feasts, and not alone on the silvery morsels. Her triumphs, too, are as food, filling her with a daily mounting eagerness for the kill.

Not immediately did she become the proficient hunter where this new prey was concerned. At first, many of her leaps went unrewarded. While the frightened minnow scurried to safety, she would return, cheated, to her weed-bed cover. But it would not be long before the sight of a sleek young shiner or school of precocious blunt-heads would induce her to try again. And if, on this occasion, her aim was true and her timing right, a fierce satisfaction would possess her.

For a time she gave herself up to practice, catapulting into a minnow pack and leaving four and five of its members dead with as many slashes of her jaws. But soon the demands of hunger left no room for such prodigality. From then on she killed singly, pausing to turn one victim and swallow it head first before seizing the next.

Crippled minnows she ignored, even those that managed to struggle free from her own teeth. The healthy ones that sought to escape and had the power to do so—these were the ones that interested her. And, as there were plenty of them, she could continue to humour the selective traits with which Nature had endowed her.

Large-mouth bass fry also fell to her jaws during this period. But she had, herself, to beware of Leaper, the big male bass with yawning mouth that could engulf a bull frog with ease, who, for a time, shepherded his offspring along the shoreline. There were many such bass in the marsh but, as a rule, they stayed in the shade of the lily-pad clusters. Moreover, were they afield, the telltale black band that ran transversely down each side of their deep-chested rush-green bodies made them easy to avoid.

Even more was it necessary to beware of rock bass and perch. For Ma-Kee, growing daily though she was, was still no match for these rival predators of the moment. And, in the marsh, they far outnumbered all other finned inhabitants except sunfish and minnows.

Once, as twilight set in over the marsh, its cold gleam discovering Ma-Kee in the act of seeking cover for the night, a dark form hurtled towards her. It was a rock bass and, fleeing not a second too soon, she barely escaped with her life. Late evening was the red-eyed one's favourite feeding time.

Another time she is sharply reminded that she is not the only one of her species in the marsh.

The day has been bright and windless: a combination not to Ma-Kee's liking, for it is difficult to stalk prey under such conditions. Twice she had managed to get close to minnow flocks, only to be discovered before she could gather herself for a leap. She has not eaten since the previous day and her stomach demands to be filled.

At last a little group of shiners makes its way towards her. She feels her muscles tightening but controls herself so that not the slightest quiver of fin or body will betray her presence there beside the frond of feathery milfoil.

Nearer. . . . Nearer. . . . She is preparing herself for the leap when suddenly, like a thrown dart, a slim fin-propelled shape flashes between her and her advancing quarry. Another

muskellunge is ahead of her and, in an instant, has successfully transfixed the leading shiner between two sets of rose-
thorn teeth.

The intruder is a male, only two-thirds the size of Ma-Kee,
but strong and confident. With the shiner half-gorged, he
moves to return to the shelter of the weeds. As he does so,
a shudder goes through him, for Ma-Kee's jaws have suddenly
closed on his body, burying a series of pain-inflicting barbs
in his flesh.

A moment ago he was the attacker—now the attacked.
Thus the quick change of fortunes in this uncertain world.

He tries to disgorge the shiner in order to turn on Ma-Kee,
but cannot. In any event, strong though he is, he is not her
equal. She has him fast and it is only a question of time. No

qualms assail Ma-Kee as, a short while later, she succeeds in getting her blood brother, shiner and all, part way down her gullet.

There is only one law in the marsh, a law she has come to know full well up to this point: *everything that lives, tries to remain alive; and to remain alive requires all the wiles at one's command.* It is as simple as that.

Her every action, her every aggression, her every defence, are in full harmony with this law.

In early November of the year she was born, Ma-Kee left the Great Marsh. The event was a turning point in her life for it meant that she was now large enough to face the dangers of the lake—her true home.

The marsh had been a highly satisfactory haven up to that point. Its gentle waters had cradled her. Through its subterranean gardens had ranged a food supply befitting her size and requirements. And its perils, while many, were proportionate to her ability to cope with them.

But now the time had come to forsake the marsh, like a cast-off shell, for the greater attractions of the world beyond.

Where the marsh opened onto the lake a broad plain of rippled sand had formed, its white surface disturbed only occasionally by moss patches and thwarted weed growths. Around this area, in a semi-circle, the bottom dipped into normal shallows, and in due course the weeds began.

It was on the fringe of the weeds, a short distance from the marsh entrance, that Ma-Kee stayed the winter. She would have liked to venture farther, but experience had made her cautious. The horizonless expanse of lake, falling away into ever darkening depths, held unknown terrors. Here, at least, in the sunlit shallows, she could see her enemies clearly and without effort. And in the weed fringe she herself could lie unnoticed by the shore-dwelling creatures upon which she preyed.

True, as the time of the shadow approached, her weed-bed refuge began to moulder and she was forced to resort to such supplementary shelter as sticks and rock ledges. But the weeds did not disintegrate entirely. And, always, the spongy network of their reduced state gave forth some form of life on which to feed.

Had the occasional butterfish or bass minnow not favoured her by venturing close under shore ice on sunny days, she would have gone in search of them. But now the sharp edge was gone from her appetite. No longer did prodding stomach supply the fuel of hunger to jaws and fins and brain. The slow-marching months of barrenness and decay had been accompanied by an equivalent slowing up of her digestive processes, and sometimes she would lie for days without foraging.

Hers was a state of semi-hibernation. She awaited she

knew not what. Was this unwelcome atmosphere to be the perpetual state of her new home? Was she never again to know the life-teeming splendour of her marsh existence?

Spring brought the answer to both questions. The departure of the groaning night creature, the awakening of her shadow world with a sudden inpouring of golden light, the emergence from mud tombs of insects and crustacea, the reappearance overhead of terns and other water birds—these, in concert, revived her spirits and sent her swimming with renewed energy through a new and different world.

Now Ma-Kee had seen the year around. She had experienced the peculiar effects of the seasons on her water world: the periods of light and shadow, of plenty and scarcity, of activity and inactivity, of changing temperatures and the changing mode of living they brought about. She was ready now to begin the cycle again.

As to a magnet, the minnow tribes began to move to the warm shore waters of the lake. Ma-Kee, haunting the fringe of new-grown elodea, fed as she never had before. Her appetite had returned in full measure, and with it her zest for the kill.

Sprightly May breezes, forerunners of a steady wind yet to be spawned by a low-lying cloud bank in the southern sky, chase through the fields bordering the lake. A wide area of meadow grass is suddenly combed flat, and then, just as suddenly, regains its former state. Slender willow shoots, burdened by plump buds, respond resiliently to the unseen urging. And now, as though they were pleased witnesses to the scene, the leaves of a poplar tree set up an animated clatter.

On the sandy shore edge a sandpiper has seen a midge and scurries quickly towards it. But the breeze catches the tiny insect at the crucial moment and sends it waterwards. Still hopeful of snaring the tidbit of which it has been deprived, the sandpiper follows eagerly, now running, now pausing, over sticks and clamshells and ablaqueated tree roots, finally springing agilely onto a dead tree stump overhanging the water.

In almost the same motion his beak traps the midge in mid air. The split-second, brilliant timing of the capture, to the pert grey bird perched on its tree-stump vantage point, is all in the day's work. It is about to return to the shore when its attention is attracted by a curious sight in the water.

At a distance, a black shape moves over the white sand of the shallows in the way that a throng of starlings moves low against a pale evening sky. Now and then it becomes serpent-like, but a serpent that has the power to alternately swell out like a balloon and then attenuate in a long straggling length, both retreating and advancing within itself, yet, as a whole, continuing implacably forward.

The sight is too much for the sandpiper. With a frightened spring it takes to the air, piping its alarm in piercing notes and, wheeling, is soon far down the beach.

It is not the first time that undulating, shore-haunting shapes such as this have given fright. Nor will it be the last. Many an angler frequenting the lake has experienced an involuntary shudder coincident with his first view of the nightmarish object. One such witness, indeed, whose most frequent companion was his whisky bottle, had reacted to the startling sight by hastily jettisoning what remained of the amber fluid : the supposed cause of the phenomenon.

But there is little reason for even the most timid creature —bird, man, or beast—to take fright. For, as the serpent draws near the stump, it proves to be a harmless she-catfish with her brood.

Noturus is a pond-cat of a pound in weight. On her back and sides her scaleless satin skin is black as night, milk-white on her belly, and buttery-yellow midway. Her eyes are small and white-ringed, set far apart on her massive, bull-like head.

A handsome fish when examined feature by feature, even to the sensitive, taste-bud-lined barbels which adorn both upper and lower jaws and which give her a curiously oriental look. Not her least prepossessing feature is the inside of her mouth, which she displays in all its immaculate whiteness when she stirs up the mud bottom and sucks in the food particles thus made available.

Early in May she had selected an open spot in the weeds and there, with several males in attendance, had liberated her complement of incipient offspring.

Following the hatching a fortnight later, in a demonstration of maternal regard unmatched in the fish world, she assumed guardianship of the tadpole swarm she had brought into being. She guided them, always in the safety of shore waters, to feeding grounds. She lay with them in the sunlit shallows while they played or packed in tightly around her, content for the moment to cease their perpetual-motion wriggling and, like their mother, bask in comfort. And if attack threatened, even to the smallest straggler among the hundreds that formed her brood, her mother's heart became fiercely defiant and her lithe body a barbed engine of defence.

Noturus's dual-purpose pectoral and dorsal fins were advantages peculiar to her species. Each possessed a bony spine, cruelly sharp, attached to her body by a sort of hinge. When she swam, the spines worked back and forth with her fins like arms. But when she wished, she could bring them erect and maintain them there, rigidly immovable.

Trouble lay ahead for the attacker who got her crosswise in his jaws. For there she would likely stay, transfixed, until one or the other gave up the struggle. Even then, it was almost certain death for both.

In another few days her offspring, now miniature replicas of their mother, would commence to leave her of their own accord. Meanwhile, they are still in her care and her job of the moment is to find a satisfactory weed-bed shelter for the night.

Swinging away from the sand shoal, the strange company approaches an inviting growth of water weed. As it draws alongside, one of the tragedies against which Noturus is constantly on her guard, occurs. A long slim fish, slate-grey in the fading sunlight, darts from the weed bed and in an instant is in the very thick of Noturus's youngsters, gobbling them up right and left.

The meal, while welcome, is not exactly pleasant to Ma-Kee. Each little catfish instinctively calls into play its armature of weapons and it is as though her mouth is full of sharp bits of reed. Still, she gets the squirming creatures down and is bent on consuming more when a stabbing pain in her side warns her there may be more in this encounter than she has bargained for.

She has reckoned without the leader of the pack. Indeed, she had assumed that by then the whiskery shepherdess had scuttled off, taking with her as many of her flock as she could manage. Instead, Ma-Kee has become a target for Noturus's rapier side-fin in the latter's instinctive move to protect her brood.

Ma-Kee has a lot to learn. Bullheads are a new class of animal in her life. As yet she has no notion that, despite her her own size and formidableness, there are creatures, seemingly far less redoubtable, that nevertheless earn respect.

In retaliation she turns on Noturus, seizing the soft tail end of the bullhead sideways in her jaws. That is almost as foolhardy a move as taking Noturus by the head. For, in the ensuing skirmish, the bullhead threshes whip-like back and forth, many times accidentally stabbing her enemy with her sharp pectoral spine.

Desperately Ma-Kee hangs on. Were she not still immature, such a strange predicament would not have been thrust upon her. Her opponent would have been vanquished with ease; and swallowed into the bargain.

As it is, she has no taste for the battle and a moment later releases her hold and turns tail. An ignominious retreat. Yet the series of hurts in her belly and side are reason enough.

Down in the bottom ooze, at a respectable distance, Ma-Kee nurses her wounds. Her injuries are painful but not serious. As would be the case throughout her career, she would rise from defeat.

The Prickly Fish

A WEST wind is rising on the lake. Already, in the open stretches, it has set the water to dancing briskly. But along the shore where obstacles of one kind and another constantly slow its course, it merely ruffles the surface. Its influence, therefore, does not conceal from a passing herring gull a curious disturbance on the water below.

Over an area several yards in extent, out where the coontail forests begin, the water wears an almost frightened look. It trembles with a thousand tiny pulsations, like the beating of rain. Yet there is no rain. There is only the sensation of turmoil. And the gull, dropping lower on heavy grey wings, knows it is in luck. It has seen such disturbance many times before, and has been present for the feasts that followed.

Now the gull, from a hovering position, dips deft head towards the water and seizes a shining object in its bill—and the source of the disturbance is revealed. A school of venturesome minnows is being attacked by perch. The greedy, black-barred yellow devils are gorging to the full, taking every advantage of this rich opportunity.

They are everywhere in the minnows' serried ranks, round, gauze-like mouths almost constantly agape, thrusting to right and left, above and below. Craws stuffed with silvery booty, they still carry on the attack, disgorging dead or crippled minnows in the excitement, quickly replacing them with others. It is these dead and crippled fish which, appearing from time to time on the surface, form the attraction for gulls and terns.

It is a full-scale slaughter. The minnows are numerous, and when it is all over, the survivors may even forget what has happened. Unfortunately, this will not be for some time yet, as the rearguard of the perch troop is just now going into action. And there are still the stragglers.

It seems, however, that the perch must pay a price for their feast. For the excitement has attracted several bass and muskellunge and, in no time at all, the perch column has a few less stragglers.

The bass cruise unconcernedly about, making no attempt to conceal themselves. The muskellunge, true to their nature, choose to take their prey by stealth, seeking the camouflage of the weeds, enjoining the shadows to conspiracy. From vantage point to vantage point they move, as wolves move on a flock of sheep. In such a mêlée, where all but the minnows are more concerned with their stomachs than with their skins, so extreme a show of caution seems wasted.

But for all their display of hunting form, the muskellunge are not backward in the kill. From time to time there is a vicious swirl. Silver-tinged ropes of water curl past grim snout. Jaws are swiftly opened, gill covers wide-thrown. Neatly, the perch is engulfed, pinioned, crushed, suffocated —all in one movement.

A satisfying finality accompanies the action. So quickly has the goal been achieved, the placid-faced victim has had no time to contemplate its impending demise. And when the attack is over, the gaunt assailant returns to the sidelines, there to complete the assimilation of the victim and keep sharp eyes open for fresh quarry.

In the main, the intruders are content to confine their attentions to the smaller perch. For, like Noturus, the perch family was favoured with a dorsal fin of considerable defensive value. But how different from Noturus's: here, in place of a single spear-like prong, were a dozen slender spines, linked in a graceful curve by a tough, gauzy webbing. Lying flat, in the manner of a folded fan, the spines could do no damage. Raised, they presented as formidable an aspect as a picket fence. Not without reason was it desirable to swallow Yellow-Sides head first.

The larger perch in the pack average ten inches in length and a half-pound in weight. The leader of the pack is almost twice that size, and it is he who exacts the fiercest toll. Throngs of minnows continually flee his hurtling, bull-necked form. His thrusts are quick and sure. His back fin, when an enemy nears, towers menacingly.

Perca has survived many battles. While his teeth are so small as to act merely as a rasp to hold his prey, and were never meant for offence, he behaves as if he were wholly invincible. Somehow, by bringing his saw-edged opercles into play, together with his dorsal fin, he could stave off attack fully as well as those lake inhabitants that gloried in the possession of well-equipped jaws. Thus, he was inclined to treat with disdain even the largest of possible attackers.

His surprise, then, must be complete when he is now suddenly seized about the middle and a determined attempt is made to force sharp incisors through his tough-scaled exterior. Pressure of his attacker's jaws allows him no opportunity to elevate his dorsal. And what good, at the moment, are his gill covers?

Perca's size and strength, however, suffice to extricate him from his predicament. Ma-Kee, fresh on the scene, and of a mind to enjoy a more filling repast than her usual minnow diet, has attacked rashly. How rashly, she soon knows. A deceptively small head, emerging from a weed clump, had spurred her to leap without waiting to determine Perca's full proportions.

She is aware of her error the moment her jaws close on Perca. The black-barred fish is too thick through to afford her a good grasp and, in the ensuing struggle, she feels her hold loosening.

Now Perca is free and he wheels to face Ma-Kee, back bristling. Cat-and-dog fashion, they confront one another. Neither has won, neither has lost, yet neither has the inclination to pursue the battle. Another few moments of glowering inaction will permit them to call an end to hostilities and go their separate ways without loss of dignity. But they are saved the necessity.

From above comes the sound of a boat. Instantly, the furious activity in the vicinity of the minnows ceases. The perch, scattering in sudden alarm, vanish miraculously into the weeds. The bass bolt, as though shot from cannon, furrowing the surface as they go. Besides Ma-Kee, only a few older muskellunge had remained to feed, and these also depart hastily, with the wisdom of experience.

Only a swirl of water marks where Perca had been a moment before. Ma-Kee, the lone gladiator in the arena, is content to sink to a lower level where she is well hidden but can still keep an eye on what is happening above.

The boat is closer now, and soon she sees its shadow glide effortlessly up and down over the spiked columns of the weed forest.

Ma-Kee's relationship with the world of birds and boats is a peculiar one. At any angle from her eye greater than forty-five degrees, the lake surface turns back the light rays, causing it to act as a vast mirror in which are reflected various aspects of her own underwater scene. The remaining circular area above her permits the passage of the light rays. Through this opening, as if through a window, she can see the outside world and some of its activity.

Thus, at a distance, she sees only the bellies and feet of surface-swimming creatures, with no hint of what they are like above. When they swim into her window they become whole. But although there is no way of her knowing, she does not see them in their true shapes. The bending of the light rays when they leave the water causes the resultant images to be distorted.

Boats are as familiar to her as water birds except that, because of their huge size, she sees less of them. Despite their size she has come, gradually, to view them without suspicion. Some speed by overhead with a frightening roar, displaying a single whirling propeller that glints in the sunshine and churns the water into foam. Some, long and slim, coast by silently, pushed by one broad paddle. Others, more squat, have two oars, stretching far out from their bodies. All are fearsome because of their size. But so far none have indicated that they have seen her or have any desire to attack her. Not at any time, for instance, has she seen one dive beneath the surface. And she has felt safe enough even to follow them at a distance and watch their curious movements.

The boat now overhead she watches until its body has passed out of her limited view and only its oars and under-side are to be seen. Presently even these are out of sight, and she can dismiss it from her mind.

Besides, there is something else, now, to demand her attention. At first, just a gleam tells her to be on the alert. Then the gleam, coming from the open water above the weeds, resolves itself into the firm rounded body of a chub, swimming in her direction.

Her encounter with Perca had ended in disappointment. But now she is in luck. She will have no trouble at all making this kill . . .

Gathering herself, she follows the chub's progress. Only now does she notice that the approaching fish is behaving oddly, swimming with a peculiar weaving motion that takes it in long sloping tangents, first to one side, then the other.

Now her intended victim is directly above her. It appears to have a slender reed in its mouth—an incongruity. But such incongruities apparently call for neither hesitation nor speculation. The delicious-appearing mouthful, now so tantalizingly close, calls for action.

The capture is simple. Her swift curving leap brings her alongside the chub and with a single snap of her jaws the prize is hers. Coasting to a stop, she is momentarily gratified by feeling the chub's feeble struggles in her mouth. Then, like a dog with a bone, she slowly swims back to the hiding place she had left a few short moments before.

As she reaches it, she is conscious that she is towing a reed (the same one she had seen in the chub's mouth?) but the most exasperated shake of her head fails to dislodge it. Well, she will swallow the chub and it, too, if there is no other way of getting rid of the annoyance. She succeeds in partly gorging the chub when she feels a stinging sensation in her upper jaw and her head is jerked sharply upward.

What strange happening is this? Can the insignificant fish she is in the act of swallowing be responsible? The formerly limp reed has become transformed into a thing of life and energy and is intent on towing *her*.

Fright takes hold of her. Turning in the opposite direction to which she is being pulled, she rushes off at breakneck speed. At this tactic the resistance lessens, but the live thing pressing against her snout still evinces disconcerting strength.

Assuredly this whole disturbing chain of events has some connection with the strange-acting chub now reposing part way down her gullet. If she can get rid of the chub she will be free of the reed, too . . .

But how?

The eons compressed into the development of her species answer the question for her. Involuntarily, when the pace is beginning to tell, and when she knows she must slacken her speed, she charges upward, throwing herself into the thin air above. This is the thrilling manoeuvre that characterizes the great fighting fish known by name and reputation to the anglers of a continent. This is the evidence of a fighting heart that never fails to win admiration or to set the fortunate angler's pulse beating wildly. And the spell does not fail in the present case.

"A muskie!" The fisherman, alone in the boat, has shouted aloud as Ma-Kee's lithe form clears the surface. But disappointment quickly follows. There is a 28-inch length limit on muskellunge and this one looks undersized.

Shaking her head furiously in the freedom of the air, Ma-Kee manages to rid herself of the chub before she falls back into her own element. But the sharp pricking is unabated. A bony spine, perhaps, has become detached from the chub. This annoyance, too, she must overcome.

Again, as much in desperation as in calculated planning, she thrusts her body above water. Again the effort is barren of results. And now she feels herself pulled headlong back in the direction she has come. All her efforts to resist are useless. The angler, knowing his tackle will hold, is bent on boating his captive quickly.

Half-kneeling, he reels the fish close to the boat. Then, suddenly lifting his rod-arm high, he seizes Ma-Kee firmly back of the head with his free hand and lifts her from the water.

The wiry strength of the fish in his grasp, its sleek, clean lines, and the vicious jaws (upon which he keeps a respectful eye), emphasize the thrill of catching a muskellunge. But the angler has work to do. Hastily setting down his rod, he removes the hook and holds the fish alongside his folding pocket rule which he has managed to open out on the seat. A full five inches short! What a shame—and he with his fish stringer hanging empty inside the boat. Just five more inches and he could keep it.

Still . . . who will know if he does keep it? He can reduce it to fillets before returning to camp and no one will be the wiser.

The decision made, it is only a moment's work to pass the metal skewer between opercle and gills and then out through her jaws, drawing the stringer cord after. Tethered there beside the boat, Ma-Kee's life will seldom be in greater jeopardy.

But the angler's guilt has made him jumpy. He knows the penalty will be heavy should he be apprehended with his catch. Thus, a half-hour later, when he sees a fast motor-driven skiff approaching, he is thrown into a fit of nervousness lest it be the warden. Hastily untying the cord where he has it fastened through an oarlock, he reaches for the skewer and shakes Ma-Kee free.

As it turns out, it is not the warden but another fisherman, and the angler falls to commiserating with himself. Then, as malefactors will who perform righteous deeds by force of circumstance, he begins to feel exaggeratedly pleased with himself.

"Well, that's my good deed for the day," he remarks aloud as he rigs up a new bait. "It should bring me luck."

But that night he went home empty-handed. And to his neighbours his story was that he had hooked and lost quite a sizable fish, then had the bad luck to run into only under-sized ones. Of course, he had put them all back. That's the only way to make sure there'll be big ones later on.

Following her encounter with the angler, Ma-Kee was more than ever disposed to maintain her shallow water retreat. For a long while she did not permit herself to be lured by happen-ings beyond the weed fringe. The shoreline was safe. More-over, as long as summer continued, she had access to all the food she needed.

When boats came near, she slunk into her weed cover and remained there until the danger was past. She could not comprehend what had happened. But she did not wish to experience again the suffocating dryness of the air nor suffer the touch of the man-creature that rode upon the boat's back.

Gradually, however, memory of her experience grew dim, and before the first thin sheet of glare ice warned her of the approach of the annual shadow, she was venturing farther afield than ever.

One day she came upon a pair of large-mouth bass that en-joyed a particularly fine refuge beside the sunken hulk of a long-abandoned gasoline launch.

Choosing a time when the two went foraging in separate directions, she pounced on the smaller male bass and for a full day lay on the bottom gorging her captive. The bass was larger than Perca, with a not insignificant array of dorsal spines. But Ma-Kee herself had grown considerably since her encounter with the perch leader. And she had managed to grasp the bass from underneath, so that its dorsal was ren-dered ineffective.

By the time her meal was digested, the she-bass had left

the refuge, perhaps feeling that her mate had deserted her. Promptly, Ma-Kee moved in. The spot was perfect for winter operations. She could await the time of light with a greater feeling of security than she had known before. She had found a home.

Ravenor

THE first thin ice layer failed to resist November winds and, for a while, the lake was set free again. But as the winter advanced there came a day when the icy yoke held. Steadily it grew thicker. On bitterly cold days it appeared black and menacing, and snow blew in powdery clouds across its glassy surface. Then a spell of mild weather melted the snow, encrusting it, and successive snowfalls joined land and lake so that it was difficult to tell where the one left off and the other began. In the hushed twilight beneath the ice, life went on as before, but at a slower pace and with fewer participants.

Of those lake dwellers that Nature had committed to a year-round existence, insect-feeders such as sunfish and painted turtles had the easiest time of it. In the mouldered weed masses, colonies of boatmen and backswimmers could be stirred into flight simply by nosing into their labyrinthine retreats. Bottom refuse, too, nudged to one side, often revealed larval delicacies.

Predators, such as Ma-Kee, were forced to greater effort to fill their craws. But, happily, this was compensated for by the lessened demands of hunger.

Food stayed with Ma-Kee an inordinate length of time. A plump, half-pound sucker, for instance, captured one morning in early February and swallowed head first shortly after, required two days to complete the metamorphosis from whole fish to raw flesh, and the final trip of undigested matter through the pyloric valve took until the first week in March.

In the summer months, when she was active, a similar digestive performance would be accomplished in one-third the time.

Two incidents of an unusual nature occurred to break the monotony of her winter imprisonment. The first took place soon after freeze-up. On a day when the ice was still transparent, she was startled by a thunderous noise on the ice roof not far from where she lay in the security of her newly acquired hideout. The thunderous noise was followed by the sudden piercing of the roof and the plunging downward, in clear view, of four threshing sticks. Above the sticks Ma-Kee glimpsed a bulky object almost like a boat.

A stray cow, not yet stabled for the winter, had safely negotiated shore ice, only to break through the thinner layer just beyond. Now it floundered helplessly, out of depth, unable to regain the shore.

The terrifying sight sent Ma-Kee bolting far out into deep water. She did not venture to return for several hours. When she did, although there was no sign of movement from the monster, she again beat a hasty retreat. But several days later, having grown used to its presence, she was back at her usual stand.

Eventually, with the spring break-up, the cow was reduced to a skeleton. Eels and crayfish aided in the transformation—a performance distasteful to Ma-Kee. On the other hand, the eaters of dead flesh she regarded as legitimate booty, and for a long while the unfortunate animal was the means of supplying her with a sizable part of her wants.

The second occurrence took place in February when the ice was thickest and food hardest to find.

The water upon which Ma-Kee and other gill-equipped inhabitants of the lake depended for life-giving oxygen contained little oxygen of its own. Some was manufactured by aquatic plants: a process halted in winter when the ice, with its mantle of snow, shut out the sun's rays. But the main source of supply was the air mass above. Pressure of the air column, aided by wave action, drove oxygen deep into the water of the lake. It was this transmitted oxygen that the fish breathed, absorbing it into their systems through the red blood cells of their gills.

Consequently, as the winter advanced and the ice roof grew thicker, there was a diminution of the water's oxygen content. The situation was not as perilous as it would have been in summer when the warmer water encouraged activity and the need for oxygen was greater. Still there were times, particularly following hunting trips, when Ma-Kee experienced a feeling of suffocation and she would lie panting, like a dog after a run.

Then, during a period of severe cold, a pressure crack developed in the ice. Expanding rapidly, the ice pushed against itself like a live thing. Along the shores it was a solid wedge and could give but little. This meant that the energy travelled chiefly outward from both shores. Thus the eruption, when it took place, was bound to occur somewhere out on the frozen lake surface.

The weakest ice gave way first, buckling against the inexorable push, then splitting in a ragged crack that ran like a lightning streak down the lake. Shoulder to shoulder the ice masses strained, eventually falling back as the ordeal ceased, and there remained in a state of tortured upheaval.

A rumbling noise accompanied the break, followed by many sharp explosive sounds and mingled groans and creakings as the ice slowly settled into place over the length of the pressure crack. Altogether it was a most terrifying clamour, sending every underwater being within hearing distance into hiding.

Ma-Kee is among the first to venture curiously forth. The light first attracts her, for light—even the thin shafts that, here and there, manage to filter through the night creature's wound—is a welcome sight after months of semi-darkness. Then she notices that she is able to breathe more easily and she gives herself up to luxuriating in this welcome relief.

Others of the lake's inhabitants are attracted to the break, and soon an odd company of fish of all sorts, sizes, and shapes has gathered. Like actors hugging the spotlight, they swim slowly back and forth along the length of the break, caution and predatory instincts alike forgotten, eager only to experience the exhilaration that the inrush of fresh oxygen brings to them.

Ma-Kee breathes thirstily. Each jet of water forced over her gills floods her body with new energy. Unnoticed, perch and sunfish crowd by her. Once she even makes way for a minnow troop. But there is soon an end to such nonsense.

All at once she is satiated. The situation comes into proper focus and, with a full realization of the opportunity that has been presented to her, she snaps up several shiners in quick succession. A bass, close by, seizes a perch, and in a twinkling the strange assembly scatters.

For a week Ma-Kee stayed in the vicinity of the pressure crack, preying on the victims that responded to its lure. But a heavy snow shut off both light and air, and in due course she returned to her hideout, there to take up her torpid existence once again.

In the lake were many kinds of fish. Of them all, none was stronger or fiercer than Ravenor the bowfin.

Ravenor was of a family commonly called dogfish by anglers—perhaps because, when caught, they often emit a barking sound. The sound, actually, is more of a grunt, and is caused by the rapid expulsion of air from the bowfin's bladder. "Bowfin" is a more descriptive name, deriving from the long, supple fin that arches in a bow over most of the length of this fish's back. It appears, almost, to join the tail, so close is the division, with the result that bowfins are occasionally mistaken for eels.

Ravenor was a typical specimen of the family, save that he had lost an eye. His olive-green body was cylindrical in shape, encased in a sheath of round, hard scales. His head was blunt and, with its armour-plated under-jaw, strangely reminiscent of some prehistoric saurian's for, indeed, Ravenor's likeness was to be found far back in the calendar of time. He was the possessor of profuse, sharp-pointed teeth that were obviously meant for offence, and almost incredible strength to back them up.

He sported, as well, an adornment that, in a sense, could have been said to be a third eye had he, in addition, been equipped with the customary two. This adornment, the ocellus, was a prominent, dark-coloured spot surrounded by an orange-yellow halo, located at the upper base of the tail. Apart from its ornamental value, it identified him as a male fish. For, in the female of the species, this eye was hardly noticeable.

On warm, bright days in summer, Ravenor liked to lie in the surface weeds. There he would remain for hours at a time, the perpetual rippling movement of his back fin making quite the most poetic picture in all the lake. At other times, particularly when the sky was cloudy, he would pick a dark cave in the weeds beside open water, from which vantage point, like a tiger in its lair, he could spring upon passing prey.

Weighing some four pounds and having the advantage of the finest in predatory equipment, he could consider even adult perch suitable quarry. And from a defensive standpoint there were few fish his size and weight, or even larger, that would cause him to back away.

Besides, Ravenor had the added asset of bad temper, the result of losing his eye. When he was younger, a fisherman had foul-hooked him, and in the ensuing struggle the eye had been torn out. Because he could see nothing on his blind side, a great deal of food escaped him. With each disappointment his irritability grew, inciting him to greater viciousness. In turn, he became suspicious. It was necessary now to be constantly on the alert for attackers.

A day in spring, not long after the ice has gone out, finds Ravenor hunting for food with greater urgency than ever before. He has emerged from winter slack-bellied, prepared to feed heavily in order to make up for the period of enforced fasting. But no food is to be found. Due to a spell of unseasonable cold weather, shore waters, where he is accustomed to forage, remain empty. It will take a good many warm days before the minnows move in. And not until the minnow migration will the perch and smaller predator fish arrive.

It is not a pleasing situation. To make matters worse, there is as yet no growth of water weeds to furnish cover for surreptitious attacks on prey frequenting the deeper water. Against his inclination, Ravenor embarks on a lengthy foraging trip as the only way open to satisfy his needs.

Swimming cautiously, the bowfin begins his quest. But he is not used to hunting in this manner and, a full day later, except for a lone crayfish, scooped up as it emerged from its mud blanket, he has had little luck.

Eventually, Ravenor's travels bring him to the derelict boat alongside which Ma-Kee has wintered. The stern of the high-gunwaled craft is well under water, sundry rifts in its planking exposing the cavernous interior. Here, intuition tells him, may be the means of assuaging his hunger.

His intuition has led him well. For, upon entering the dark, wood-ribbed chamber, the bowfin's one eye instantly spies the limp, snake-form of an eel. A quick tail-thrust, and he has seized the eel before it can flee, gulping down the squirming creature in successive stages as a sunfish consumes a worm.

Alas, search the remainder of the hulk though he does, there are no more such easy dinners. But a meal, especially in a time of privation, is a meal. There are far worse places where Ravenor might spend the ensuing days until foraging in his normal haunts improves, and so he settles in. Other eels, and perhaps rock bass, will almost certainly be attracted to the spot in due course. When they do, he will be waiting.

Thus did the strange situation develop that found two fierce predators enjoying a common shelter almost side by side.

A full day passed before Ma-Kee, lying well back in the shadow of the boat's exterior, realized that her refuge now housed a tenant—and an unwelcome one at that. She came by the knowledge in annoying fashion.

It was her custom on occasion, when she was not on the lookout for food, to prowl about her premises. For, having wrested her new hideout from its previous owners, she considered it her personal realm, and right of ownership must be made evident to all and sundry. She had a regular beat, that took her from her usual resting place outwards along the length of the boat's rough flank and thence around the stern to a point where she gained an unhindered view of the shore waters on that side.

On this day, her beat was unexpectedly cut short. As she came opposite the broken planking, a sudden fury burst upon her.

She had approached Ravenor's lair on his blind side. The bowfin, relying on vibrations picked up and translated by his lateral line, was consumed by one impression only : that food was near. Blindly he struck, his blunt, leathery body hurtling from the dark mouth of the cavern towards the thing that was passing.

The attack sent Ma-Kee reeling. What demon of the darkness was this? In the confusion, in the brain-swimming suddenness of the onslaught, she could not tell. She could only strive frantically to steady herself, realizing as she did so that her assailant's teeth had already found a hold on her body.

But luck was with her. For the bowfin's jaws had closed on her gill cover—a virtually impregnable fortification—and it was a simple matter for her to shake free.

Wheeling, she faced Ravenor. Sight of her attacker brought her fins bristling. But Ravenor, now able to see the creature he had so rashly attacked, was unwilling to pursue the engagement. His one white-rimmed eye glaring sullenly, he slowly backed water until, at a safe distance, he was able to re-enter his lair. So far as he was concerned, the affair was over.

As the days passed, a contest developed between the two fish. Unable to accept the presence of the intruder fattening on prey that was rightfully hers, Ma-Kee moved farther towards the boat's stern. There she waited, like some grim avenger, ready to rush out into the bowfin's territory at the slightest sign of movement.

She missed a great deal of shore food in this way but may have felt a savage satisfaction in cheating Ravenor of many a tidbit that would otherwise have been his. On the other hand, there were days when the successes were Ravenor's and it was Ma-Kee who was left with an empty craw.

Whenever they saw one another, their dorsals bristled. Often they charged the same quarry, once even seizing a sucker between them and tearing the hapless creature apart like two dogs sharing a piece of meat. A spectator might well have assumed they had joined forces. But nothing was further from the truth. The two fish were natural enemies. This relationship could not change. And with Ravenor's continued occupancy of her refuge, Ma-Kee's belligerence grew.

April arrives, showering rain and sunshine alternately upon the lake. In the shelter of the boat, Ma-Kee feels the slow excitement of a world coming to life. She is not feeding well. She will have to quit her post or put an end to her rival. But whether or not she is successful in the latter course, the call of the lake is bound, before long, to summon her.

Her chance came towards evening on a particularly dark and windswept day.

The rolling, pitching motion of the shore water has subsided slightly. And Ravenor, who has not ventured forth during the daylight hours, now starts on a prowl of the nearby weeds . . . perhaps a tawny side will signal the presence of a late-feeding rock bass. It is becoming more and more difficult to see.

But two eyes are better than one. Slinking within striking range, Ma-Kee is upon the bowfin before his one eye or his lateral line give him warning. She has seen him go, and followed, recognizing her opportunity.

Ravenor at first cannot comprehend what has happened. But sudden stings inside his belly, caused by the puncturing of his soft under-hide, quickly make clear the harsh truth.

Now, too late, he may learn to make a more accurate estimate of his bothersome neighbour.

Ma-Kee's upper teeth have a hold, although not a firm one, on the bowfin's back, supporting the upthrust beak and incisors of her lower jaw. Furiously she tries to pierce the tough, scaly armour. At last she succeeds. She has a grasp now that the mightiest struggles of the bowfin are not likely to dislodge. The more Ravenor threshes and twists, the more secure becomes her grip. For, with every sideways movement of the bowfin, smaller teeth join in the work of the larger.

Never has Ma-Kee fought so grimly. Doggedly she resists every convulsive movement of her opponent; punishes him in turn with a vigorous head-shaking that momentarily robs the bowfin of fight. Her main difficulty is breathing. Her jaws are clasped tight and she can feel Ravenor's scaly side jammed suffocatingly close against her vomer. Radiating from her distended opercles, the branchiostegal rays stand out like stiffened fingers.

The battle is now carried on in utter darkness: sometimes down among the water plants, at other times on the surface. Grubbing mudcats, among the few aquatic creatures still active, pause in their tadpole wig-wagging, alarmed. A black-crowned night heron, hearing the commotion, hesitates in flight, wheels, and settles stiff-legged on the sandy shore, daring to hope that the combatants will eventually come within reach.

At length, mortally wounded, Ravenor's struggles cease.

Triumph! But is it? In Ma-Kee's fast-fading strength lies possible defeat. Feebly, slowly suffocating, she attempts to withdraw her incisors from her dying opponent, but finds the effort beyond her. She can do nothing but lie still, suffering Ravenor's lifeless body to pull her up to the surface. There they float, responding to the shoreward push of the dying wind.

On the shore, after a patient quarter-hour, the heron has its hopes rewarded. The ocellus, adorning Ravenor's tail, is Ma-Kee's salvation. Its golden outer ring, haloed in the moonlight, draws the heron's beak like a magnet. But quite a series of tugs is necessary to drag the clumsy prize to a point where it can be released and fed upon. And in the process Ma-Kee finds herself freed.

The cool water is balm on her tortured gills. In a few moments it revives her. Quickly her tail fin sends her outward into the shelter of the night.

Indian

A SUMMER day is ending. In the whole of a calm sky, light comes only from one corner, and there, submerged in an aquamarine sea, the sun has dyed the horizon a brilliant gold. But it is a chameleon colour that quickly fades.

Night now emerges from earth and sky, stealthily at first, then with sudden boldness.

In the glassy half-light a curious shape glides silkily over the water. It is a man in a canoe—an Ojibway Indian from the reservation. He has been trolling. But now, recognizing night's inevitable approach, he stops paddling and starts to retrieve his handline.

Overhead a straggling band of crows, like the remnants of a beaten army, wings towards a distant refuge. From somewhere, far up in the vault of diminishing blue, comes the harsh *kra-ark* of a heron. Nature has chosen these fleeting moments to reveal some of her rarest magic. And the Indian, Tom Bartlett, whose thinking is attuned to every manifestation of the Great Spirit, is not unaware of the spell that is being cast.

It is for this reason that he pays too little attention to the manner in which he retrieves his line. Ordinarily he would fish his lure carefully right to the boat, for one never knows when a prospective catch might be following it. Now, instead, he brings it in quickly, hand over hand, letting the line fall in irregular coils on the canoe floor.

Unexpectedly, as he lifts his lure clear of the surface a

fish breaks water after it. So eager is the fish in its attempt to capture the escaping prey that it sails right out of the water, falling to the surface with a loud splash.

The startled Indian glimpses straining jaws and the dim lines of a slim, strong body. The jaws close with a hollow snap. Then there is only disturbed water where the fish has disappeared.

Not a large fish, but assuredly of legal size or better—a "keeper."

Quickly he tosses the metal wobbler out a short distance and draws it in. Again he repeats the manoeuvre. But to no avail. The muskellunge, for it was Ma-Kee, does not relish the proximity of the boat and has returned to the weed bed where she had been lying.

The corners of the brown man's eyes crease in the barest admission that the incident has had its humorous side. He deserved the indignity of failure. The old ones who nod over the fire might so have been caught napping. Well, he knows where the fish lies. Another time, when the light is better, he will give it a chance to taste his lure.

Ma-Kee spent the night with an empty craw. Too late her stomach had bade her be after the strange, erratic-swimming fish. With its glittering body and hurrying, darting gait it had presented a most inviting appearance. But she would have found differently had she managed to get it in her jaws. The seemingly plump body would have turned out to be distastefully hard. And what had seemed to be a tail would, in reality, be stinging barbs. Success on that occasion might have spelled her finish. But she can know nothing of these things, and so can have cause only to regret the meal she has missed.

Morning saw her feeding ravenously. Before the first rays of the sun penetrated the weed forests, she had sought out a school of sleepy sand minnows and reduced their ranks by a dozen or so. Her broad tail provided the power to thrust her body successively in several directions. Her pectoral fins helped her manoeuvre to just the right degree, right or left; to stop, back up, or ease forward. Her jaws snapped decisively at the proper moment, pinioning each captive, delivering it subsequently back past vomer and palatines to the drawn muscular sack that constituted the swallowing structure of her throat.

It was a wonder that any escaped.

In the bewildering fury of her attack, a large male sunfish got in her way and with a convulsive shudder was caught in the trap. For some time she swam about with the pumpkin-seed crosswise in her mouth, looking as though she had sought its gaudy brilliance, like some bright jewel, to offset her plainness. But such illusions are alien to her life of concentrated plunder and before long she gulped down her handsome captive as readily as her other hard-won spoils.

Soon after, surfeited, she backed into a passageway in the shore weeds and let herself sink until she could feel the warm touch of the sand on her belly. There she stayed, sleeping off her meal, while the sun rose almost to overhead and the shallows became enveloped in a peaceful glaze.

Now she lies motionless, removed for the time being from the drama going on about her. She might as well have been of another world for all that it mattered. The chain of existence remains unbroken.

A yellowthroat leaves the reeds, deftly scoops up a boat bug as the scurrying insect breaks the surface for air. The gentle wave shadows caused by the commotion frighten a horse leech into changing the direction of its ribbony flight. Soon it comes on the algae-coated surface of what it takes to be a stone. A delightful browsing ground—or so it thinks. But the stone is suddenly metamorphosed into a crayfish. A broad claw snatches and seizes the leech; drags it down to where beady, elevated eyes and horny mouth can concentrate on consuming it.

Now all is peaceful again. But only for a moment. A slender midge larva has crawled onto an innocent-appearing bladder-wort sac. The slit in the side of the bean-like structure opens as though sprung by a trigger, pulling in water and larva as into a vacuum. Before the stricken creature disappears, a hydra reaches down with its stinging tentacles, catching and paralysing the larva and dragging it upward to be thrust whole into the hydra's capacious stomach.

Nothing exists down here for want of being eaten.

Ma-Kee is in her third summer and growing rapidly. The whole story of her growth is recorded on her scales.

If examined under a microscope, the unexposed portion of a scale would reveal a series of circular ridges. During the winter, when she grew but little, the ridges were close-packed. But during the summer when there was a plenitude of food and sunlight, as now, and she thrived, gaps showed between the ridges. Each gap indicated a year of her life.

Lying motionless amid the rearing pondweeds, she does not seem the same fish as the tiny fingerling that once was one of the lesser creatures of the water world. She is larger now by far, scaling six pounds and measuring two feet in length.

While still long and slim of build, her back has broadened and she is proportionately thicker through. Her fins and tail have grown. And they, in company with the tightly com- pacted union of muscle and sinew that is her body, testify to the energy she can summon on an instant for her deadly purposes.

But it is the thinking, feeding, seeing end of this lithe fin- powered creature in which the most awe-inspiring changes have been wrought. Each feature seems to have become co- ordinated with all others in an alliance that has destruction as its sole intent.

The ribbed, cartilaginous snout is now more sunken, held tightly compressed against a jutting lower jaw that is gradu- ally turning upward into an inverted beak. The opercles are wide and armour-plated, dropping off into a bellows arrange- ment of branchiostegal rays that assists the jaws to spread to their fullest extent. Even her eyes seem to have entered into the collaboration. By nature set flat to her head, they now tend to protrude from their bony casements as though pushed out from within; from which plane, coupled with her ability to tilt them up or down, forward or back, she can catch sight of prey in any direction.

And her teeth! When she opens her mouth, a regular torture chamber is revealed.

There are teeth, specially situated for grasping, clustered in the forefront of her upper jaw. There are teeth, bristling like up-ended thumbtacks, along each side of her jawbone, above and below. And as if this is not a sufficient armature, palate and vomer, too, are equipped with patches of tiny teeth, like sandpaper, all sloped conveniently inward.

It is an easy matter to enter this fortified gape. But let the victim attempt to wriggle free and a hundred miniature spear points impede its passage.

The tiger stripes that made her at home amid the bur reeds and eel grass of the Great Marsh have broadened into bars that are sometimes vivid, sometimes almost lost to sight, depending on whether the day is dull or bright and in what cover she happens to be lying. These changes in intensity of pattern are accompanied by subtle changes in coloration. So that, while she may begin the day in her customary garb of mottled grey with a mantle of blackish-green cast upon her back, before evening she will have adopted as many changes as the number of environments through which she has passed.

This faculty, unwilled, of altering colour and pattern to suit her surroundings is one of her chief predatory aids.

Who can spy her at first glance, there in her sunlit retreat? She could be a stick or a streamer of weed, so well has she mimicked the russet-green tones around her. She has a defence, too, against the glittering sand of the shallows. For the edges of her scales have the brilliance of diamonds. And later, when she is a keen watcher from the coontails, she will resort to the utmost in her repertory of camouflage to seem simply a harmless company of shadows.

For thousands of years her kind has existed in the Lakeland. Once, far back in the vaulty recesses of time, a ragged ice crust crept down over the northern part of this continent, invading the Great Lakes basin—the domain of the ancestral stock of muskellunge.

No fish could exist in the advance of the glacier. To survive, Ma-Kee's ancestors fled southward, there to take up position as best they could beyond the glacial tongue. When, unaccountably, the great cold came to an end and the ice began to retreat, the muskellunge stock became divided. Some remained in the refuge to which they had fled; some moved westward; some moved back into their former territory.

Over the ages that followed, differences in colour-pattern, as well as other differences brought about by widely separated environments, caused the three muskellunge groups to become distinct from one another as subspecies. Ma-Kee's forbears, hewing so closely to the original strain, bore the most dominant colour-pattern of all three subspecies. Of her it could be said she was a true representative of her race.

A close kin of the ubiquitous pike, the great grey fish of the north was given the name *mashk-kinonge* by Indians who first chanced upon it, indicating that it was a "different sort of pike" from the one with which they were familiar. The Indians prized the muskellunge as a food fish and came to rely on it as a main article of sustenance. But the wind of fortune blew ill when the commercial fisheries of the white man drastically reduced the ranks of the muskellunge. Especially was this so in the waters of the Lakeland where, in one season, in the year 1890, the catch ran into hundreds of tons.

The introduction of game-fish laws had the effect of further restricting their take, and the Indians were forced to rely even less upon the great grey fish. But they continued to fish for muskies when time allowed, and their art excelled that of the white man who, from afar, envied the brown man in his birchbark canoe with his crude but effective hand-line and wobbler.

The sudden blotting out of the sun by something moving above her brings Ma-Kee to startled wakefulness. A boat?

But the object, one upturned eye instantly tells her, is more fearsome than that.

Chelydra, the snapping turtle, is abroad. A she-turtle of immense age, Chelydra's horny segmented shell is as large as an overturned wash basin, and her flippers as she strokes her way slowly along seem as broad as bear paws. With her warty skin, cruel blunt head, and serpent neck she is a carryover from the reptilian era. And she is as fierce as she looks.

Her compact skull houses a brain that exists chiefly to direct the lethal actions of her body. Had she the memory, she could recall a hundred thousand kills, all consummated by the ripping, tearing agency of her claw-like beak and bony jaws. Her pitiless eyes have witnessed them all, but they are beyond her counting.

No creature in all the lake is more to be feared. Her jack-in-the-box head can strike with the rapidity of a cottonmouth. Moreover, she is virtually invincible. Few are the possessors of teeth that can pierce the leathery folds of her neck—her one vulnerable spot. And even when thus seized, she can fight unsubdued almost indefinitely.

Chelydra is a killer. She is also a robber, snatching the prey of others when the opportunity presents itself. Even dead flesh she considers fair booty.

Now, as she spies Ma-Kee, it is live flesh that occupies the attention of her pygmy brain. With marvellous agility for so clumsy a creature, she strokes downward. Sixteen inches of neck and head shoot out as though impelled by a spring. But Ma-Kee is too quick. In the interval between discovery and attack, her vitality seemed to desert her. Then, the terror that an instant before had held her powerless, releases the full flood of her energy and, with a lightning swirl, she flees.

The snapping turtle's carven jaws close disappointingly on a stream of bubbles left in Ma-Kee's wake. But Chelydra has missed before and will miss again. In between, there will be many successes.

She knows better than to attempt to pursue the fleeing muskellunge. Instead, she resumes her breast-stroking, this

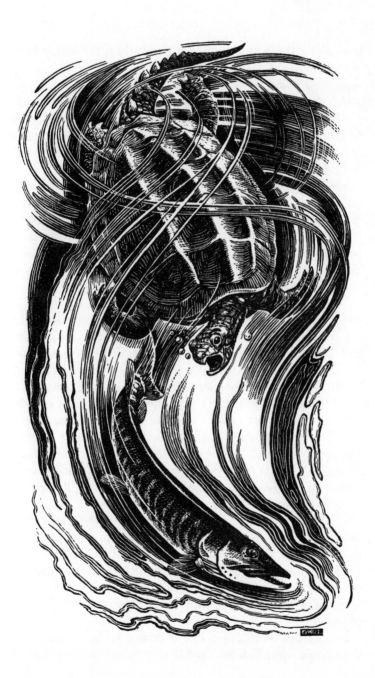

time along the bottom, and her curiously luminescent form is soon swallowed in the weeds.

A crisp breeze and overcast sky have urged the Indian forth once more. With firm strokes he has taken his canoe to a favourite bass shoal in the lee of a rock island two miles from the village. Now, in the early evening, a string of bass at his feet, he is returning.

Suddenly he is reminded of the scene of his encounter with Ma-Kee. His eyes roam the shoreline. It is not far out of his way—half a mile at most.

Swiftly he swings the canoe, accepting the challenge. Soon, perhaps, the rash attacker of his lure will know that Little Tom is not one to trifle with. And who can tell? The same water may contain even more sizable fish.

"Little Tom" was a nickname—a rare use, by the Ojibways, of the inappropriate—singling him out for his height, which was above average, also for his feats of skill and endurance in the bush and on the water. When he was a boy, he had stealthily fashioned a fish spear, giving amusement to his elders when they heard of it. But their amusement was short-lived for there came a day when he appeared excitedly before them, in his hands the spear, impaled on the tines a fish. The incident was not forgotten. Thus, when he came of age he was officially named Kah-be-wah-be-ko-kay—"maker of spears." But as he grew older the name was seldom used. When he was required to sign, as on his hunting licence, he used his adopted name, Tom Bartlett.

His family, through the male line, was of the Crane clan; in other words, used a crane as its *do-daim* or totem. The crane, like the loon and osprey, was a great fisher. And Little Tom, early mindful of the responsibility that went hand in hand with so honoured a designation, had as a boy strived to master the secrets of the waters and to become a fisherman of prowess.

In time, his skill brought him fame as a guide. Anglers from the cities sought him out, and it was in this manner that he spent most of his days during the fishing season. September saw him gathering wild rice to sell in the white man's market. Winter was a time partly for such things as fashioning lures and mending boats, and partly for resting. Canoes he made from birchbark cut in early spring when it was most easily removed from the tree, with cedar for ribs and thwarts, and the split roots of tamarack for sewing.

The life was to his liking. It was a life only slightly different from that of his forefathers. It made him as one with wind and sun and strengthened his kinship with the creatures of the wild. It roused in him, too, an understanding of his ancestors' mystic preoccupation with Nature. In the green leaf, in the snows of winter, in the cry of the loon, in the thousand wonders of the heavens, were the answers. And the great host of spirits, good and bad—who could quarrel with the fitness of such creations; even such as he who, by modern tokens, must disbelieve?

And so Little Tom went his way, dissociated from, yet splendidly mindful of, these strange influences of the past.

Ramrod straight in the canoe, sinewy body clothed in the sun-faded vestments of civilization, he is a symbol of the sixteenth-century nomad, settled down in the twentieth century to the white man's way of life. The Indian would never cease to be an Indian. While the waterways and forests remained, so would the brown man. But when they were taken away or destroyed, so would he be destroyed. Nature, and Nature alone, controlled his destiny.

Only one thing gave Little Tom cause for lament. His beloved muskellunge, the great leaping fish whose majesty matched the pine forests and broad waters of the Lakeland, was fast disappearing. He was harder put, year after year, to satisfy the customers who wanted a muskie. This in itself he minded little, for he was not entirely dependent on his earnings as a guide. But he had grown to respect and admire the great grey fish beyond the bounds of attachment ordinarily felt for lower creatures so far removed from the family of man. Thus his concern for its plight amounted to a sorrow.

The canoe has slowed now, having come to the weed bed. Overboard goes the wobbler.

Little Tom trolls in the time-honoured fashion of the Indian: line twisted about his wrist, then around the paddle. As the paddle moves, the lure darts forward, halts, darts forward again. He is in luck. Ma-Kee sees the wobbler and is after it in a rush.

Here is the curious fish again. This time it shall not escape! She has it in her mouth now, feeling its hardness against the gristled underside of her snout. It is not nearly so satisfying as she had hoped. Too, its spiny tail is hurting her in a way unpleasantly like her encounter with the prickly fish.

Well, down it goes, whether it tastes good or not. But try as she will she cannot dislodge her unwelcome mouthful. It has secured a hold and will not stir.

A new discovery shuts out all other considerations. It is necessary to exert all her energy to prevent being dragged along by the strange fish. This will not do.

Taking the initiative, she turns and runs furiously in the opposite direction. But a slow pressure on her head finally brings her up, panting, content merely to pursue the fight in a series of stubborn tug-of-war manoeuvres that take her in wide sweeps from side to side.

The Indian, meanwhile, is hunched quietly in the canoe, giving or taking line when need be, prepared for whatever may occur. His string of bass he has lowered over the side to make room for action. His paddle lies against a thwart.

At any moment he expects to see the muskellunge hurtle upward in a head-shaking leap. Ma-Kee, however, is not yet ready to resort to such tactics. Instead she sounds, burying herself in weeds and mud, and stays there.

It is an old pike trick, knowledge of it having been impregnated in her make-up despite the gulf in the blood lines of the two fish. Not often does it work. For, all the angler is required to do is sit and wait. But as luck would have it, this time it saves her skin.

In the canoe Little Tom, patiently biding his time, grips the line between his knees and reaches in his pocket for his tobacco. As he does so, a movement at the side of the boat attracts his attention.

He needs but a glance to tell him what is happening. With a fierce animal leap he comes to his feet, clutching the paddle in the same movement. Raising the paddle shoulder high, he slashes with its edge at something in the water.

"Tah yah!" he shouts angrily. "Mother of a water rat! Robber!"

It is Chelydra. Sounds of the battle had brought her to investigate. Surreptitiously, during the lull, she has made a meal of Little Tom's catch of bass. She has eaten well. Only the heads remain.

The paddle blade glances harmlessly off her shell. For an instant her stony eyes and parted mouth show fight. But she thinks better of it. Already partly submerged, she sets her flippers back-pedalling and in a trice has scurried downward to safety.

Little Tom shakes the remnants of his catch after her retreating form.

"The stew pot shall have you for this, old she-turtle!"

The castigation still on his tongue, a further misfortune befalls him. Ma-Kee, no longer restrained by the line, chooses that moment to make her aerial sortie. With the accompanying tossing of her head she manages to fling the wobbler clear. In the gathering darkness it is all he can do to scoop up his line before it has sunk out of sight in the water.

Before he has completed the journey home, the night wind has chased the dark thoughts from Little Tom's head and he is smiling at a star that seems to smile with him.

The Channel

AND now comes a slow march of days, fiercely alight, living out their existence under a sky-belly of almost perpetual blue. This is the crescendo of summer: a shimmering note held long and sweet, seeming never to break. As if from the reed flute of Pan, it summons all to throw off the yoke of care and join in the pleasures of sun and water.

Power craft race about like whirligigs, exhilarating in the sheer joy of movement. Picnickers seek the solace of solitude on small pine-clustered islands. Swimmers splash in shore waters or laze on sparse patches of sun-warmed sand. Only the fisherman shies from the day's keen stare, preferring the evening hours when the weather is more agreeable and his bait more tempting.

On the lake a new activity is added to the many that year after year have moulded its summer guise. In a marshy bay set well back from the main body of the lake, two fisheries-research men are at work. They are university students, breaking the ground for a proposed study of the muskellunge.

A few interested sportsmen in one of the large cities had taken up the cause of the muskellunge. It was time, they said in representations to the Ontario Department of Lands and Forests, that some attempt was made to halt the decline of this important gamefish.

Maintenance of water levels during the muskie spawning season was a vital factor. Too often spawn had rotted on the shores owing to the injudicious dropping of lake levels by dam-keepers. But that was a federal Department of Transport matter, and representations in that direction had been made time without end. A 28-inch length limit ensured that muskies would reach spawning age before being taken by anglers. Poaching and other forms of lawbreaking were being checked to the extent that fisheries policing would allow. The remaining area for consideration—and an important one—was restocking.

Young muskellunge, products of artificially spawned adult muskies taken in nets, were being raised at a provincial government hatchery not many miles from the Lakeland hub. But stocking waters with these small fish was looked upon askance.

Such immature greenhorns, it was argued, having behind them only the experience of artificial ponds free of predators, were sitting ducks for anything large enough to feed on them. And to raise them to a larger size in the hatchery ponds, before planting, was out of the question. Minnows, the only satisfactory muskie food, were just not that plentiful.

New tactics were needed. Obviously another set of circumstances must be created in which muskie stocks could be brought along to a larger size before planting. How, and where, were the all-important questions.

There was no guarantee, of course, that planting adult or near-adult muskies would prove to be the answer. For one thing, the method would be expensive; far too expensive, perhaps, per pound of fish eventually recovered by anglers. The rearing of large fish from hatchery stock would require attendant research work. How many small fish were planted? How many survived the first year? The second? The third? The planted fish would need to be tagged, their growth rate kept tab on; if in an area inhabited by natural stock, population checks taken. And so on. And on top of all this there was the transporting of fish to the outer lakes, and the need, subsequently, for a creel census to determine the effect of the introductions on anglers' catches.

Where was the money to come from for all this? If available, there was still the matter of the site. A body of water of just the right type for such an operation would have to be found. It would have to be deep enough to harbour large fish. It would have to have plenty of forage fish. If a river, it would need to be dammed; if a lake, it would have to be suitable for seining. It would have to be of such a nature that it could be readily closed to fishing.

Such a body of water was, at the moment, nowhere in sight. But the idea was well worth pursuing. To get a start, a compromise project was suggested: a preliminary study of small muskies in a natural, confined area. The sportsmen would even make an effort to finance such a study, they said, provided the Lands and Forests Department would direct it. Some good was bound to come from the research work at least, even if the larger project remained just a hopeful vision. Perhaps, in the end, research—the means of finding out more about the fish they wanted to help—would prove to be their most valuable contribution.

Long on interest, but short on funds for such purely speculative ventures, Department officials were eager to support the project. And so, with high hopes, the first exploratory steps were taken.

The bay selected by the biologists for their operations is a muskellunge breeding ground—a fact determined by a scouting trip in May. It is fronted by a large island which, after wire screening has been run from either end to the shore, has provided them with the means of completely enclosing the area. The two men have spent several days seining the bay, ridding it of coarse fish and cataloguing their catch. Today will be their last haul before going on to other things.

They have set the net, paying it out from a large, square-sterned punt. The lead weights drop to the bottom, leaving a semicircle of water ringed with oblong wood floats. Now, rigged in waist-high waders, they enter the water and begin to draw the net shoreward.

Just then a canoe appears around a protruding clump of

birch trees marking one side of the bay entrance. In it is Little Tom.

He brings up the canoe with a sharp backstroke of his paddle. His eyes at first cannot believe.

The net is far too large to pass as a minnow seine. It is patently for big fish. These strange white men, then, are stealers of fish. They are like the greedy fox in a chicken pen, not content with a fair share, killing far beyond their needs.

Incredible. It is many years since Tom has witnessed poachers go about their evil work so openly. Still, he cannot be sure. In general he has learned to respect his white neighbours. Some there are, like his own kind, that cannot be trusted. But the majority have open faces and motives of goodwill.

The belly of the net is now to shore. The noise of fish congregated in close quarters can be heard. The wild threshing tumbles and splashes the water.

Suddenly Little Tom's fears are confirmed. For one of the men reaches down and with a little effort lifts a large muskellunge. He holds it up to admire its taut shimmering length, then sloshes through the water to where a holding net is secured. Into this temporary repository, against the time when specimens can be examined, he drops the muskellunge.

That is enough. As the men for the first time become aware of his presence, Tom noses his canoe into a port in the barrier and there, within speaking distance, he stops.

"You kill!" he says fiercely. "Fish not have chance. You not wanted here. Go 'way."

The two men look at one another, then burst out laughing.

"Now hold on, Joe," protests the taller of the two men, evidently the one in charge. He folds his arms, still smiling, hinching his rolled-up shirt sleeves while he seeks words. "You've got us all wrong. We're not poachers. We intend to establish a sanctuary here. Study muskie."

The explanation has no effect on Little Tom. In this outraged instant it is the blood of his savage Chippewyan ancestors that is in his veins, not that of the placid Ojibway. His mind is not open to reason, even if he could comprehend.

"Go 'way," he repeats. "Few muskie now. Net not help. Go 'way."

He has said his piece. To stoop to argument would weaken the force of his pronouncement. Backing out of the port, he straightens the canoe and is soon gone around the bend.

He need not have given the matter concern. In a few weeks, funds ran out and the project was abandoned. Those lake people who got wind of the details shrugged.

Muskies? Why worry? There would always be muskies. Besides, you could always catch bass. And a new fish, the walleye or pickerel planted in the upper lakes several years before, was beginning to show up through the system.

Little Tom, learning the truth about the university research workers, was saddened. Perhaps he would meet again with the tall man and his companion. Then he would open his heart to them.

With the coming of fall, Ma-Kee left the shoreline and headed out into the lake. The cool water gave her the urge to travel.

She kept to the weeds as an animal keeps to the forest, aware of their sheltering friendliness.

At first, there were only the familiar shallow-water weeds: coontail and elodea and, now and then, rising like ferns from a grassy bank, lone clusters of feathery milfoil. Then, as the bottom fell away to greater depths, a jungle of rusty, rumpled leaves attached to clumsy stalks reared precipitously surfaceward. This was a ruffle-leaf pondweed bed, of which there were many in the lake.

Always this weed was dominant, establishing ownership of the deeper sections, itself intimidated only by depths greater than twenty feet. The beds often stretched acres in extent, towering rich and luxuriant in June; clogging the surface with trailing stems when the water level dropped.

Beloved of fishermen as the favourite hiding place of muskellunge, the tough, liana-like weeds were nevertheless the bane of propeller-driven craft, the screws of which were forever becoming entangled in the thick morasses. Even now, despite the lateness of the season, they retained a tenacious hold on life. But in a matter of weeks they would start to die down, and winter's arrival would see their disintegration completed.

On the edge of the pondweed forest Ma-Kee paused, gill covers distended. Faintly she sensed the movement of water. It was no more than a suspicion, conveyed to her like the gentlest of breezes, yet her instincts told her that somewhere beyond the maze of weeds a powerful current was flowing.

Because the sensation was new, she felt a heady inclination to track the mystery to its source. On and on she pressed. She swam slowly, pausing every so often to rest and take stock of her surroundings.

Once she blundered into a pack of catfish drifting like an inky cloud a few feet beneath the surface. They were larger than their shore relatives, with massive heads and slender grey-flanked bodies. Alarmed, they dived for the bottom, plummeting frantically around her in such numbers that all she could see was a flurry of wriggling eel-shapes.

It was a hailstorm of catfish and it was over quickly. To move while it was on would have meant being slashed in a hundred places by stiletto-sharp pectoral and dorsal armaments. And so, stoically, Ma-Kee held her place, proceeding only after the pack had dissolved into nothingness beneath her.

On and on. Now and again she spied bass and muskellunge and, occasionally, new large golden-scaled fish with dark backs and perch-like dorsals. These were the walleyes, future Lakeland dwellers of prominence.

Darkness fell to mark the end of her first day's journeying. Overhead, in ascendancy, the seven stars of the Pleiades climbed high in the eastern sky, soon to be lost amid the glittering gallery of rival constellations. A wind sprang up and, in the pale glow of the October moon, the lake looked lonely.

On shore, only a few lights remained. Most of the summer residents had closed their cottages and returned to the city. Only the Indian reservation at the lakehead gave indication that the area was populated to any extent by man, and even there, one by one, the feeble flickerings of kerosene lamps were soon extinguished. The Ojibways, except on the occasion of council meetings or festivals, were not ones for late hours.

The next day saw Ma-Kee in different territory.

Abruptly, where the pondweeds ended, an island grew up out of the lake. There, in a small bay where the rocky shoreline was relieved by sparse patches of pinweed, she rested, taking toll of the stupid black-chinned shiners that assembled there on warm days, even so late in the season. Her accustomed haunts had not delivered prey more readily, and she ate her fill before moving on.

Past the point of the island, the rock descended into the water in a series of longitudinal ridges, the intervening crevices having the appearance of being gouged out by huge claws. These were the marks of the glacier, to be seen, as well, in many places on the mainland. Out from here lay the lonesome depths: a yawning hole, many hundreds of feet across, that loomed dark and formidable no matter how bright the weather.

Many stories were told about this hole by local residents and summer cottagers alike. It was, the stories went, bottomless. And in it, it was said, were the remains of victims of drowning whose bodies had never been recovered.

It was reported (in jest by most) that a fearsome creature dwelt there; a fish, perhaps, of tremendous proportions, with a black and ugly head and the body of a serpent. It had once been hooked, but toward nightfall, and no one had had a really good look at it. In the ensuing battle the rowboat containing the unlucky fisherman had been upset and he had barely escaped drowning, which lent further credence to the tale.

That it was something more than a fish, Old Nogee, aged Ojibway headman, was ever ready to affirm with a knowing look and a muttered supplication to Mon-e-doo. The Spirit of the Fishes dwelt in the lake and took many strange forms. Did not the mist hang more heavily over this spot than others? Had he not seen Maung, the loon, dive there, never to surface again? And once great bubbles welled up, unexplained. Surely it was a place to avoid.

The truth, hidden even from the creatures that from time to time ventured into the lonesome depths, was somewhat less fantastic.

The murky, gaseous bottom did hold human remains, but not of recent times. On a dark summer night some three hundred years before, a raiding party of Iroquois, intent on surprising a Huron encampment, was taken unawares by the intended victims. War canoes side to side, fierce cries rending the air, the Hurons fell upon their hated enemies in so complete a slaughter that not one of the raiding party escaped.

The bodies of the Iroquois braves who drowned or who were slain littered the bottom in the vicinity of the lonesome depths. Eventually their bones, and even some of their weapons, responding to the inexorable bottom swell, found their way into the hole. And there they stayed, never quite covered by the shifting ooze; here a shinbone protruding, there a skull, with war spear and tomahawk keeping them constant company as the weapons of departed warriors should.

And the monster . . . well, it would have been a disappointment to the grizzled Ojibway tale-teller to know that it was not a monster after all, but merely a rather ancient specimen of catfish. True, it had a black and ugly head, and its body was serpent-like. But all channel catfish of any size answer that description.

Ictalurus, content amid the awesome debris far down in the lonesome depths, and feeding only at night, would continue to arouse speculation in any who chanced on her. She, who had once snared a diving loon and held on until it drowned, would not easily give in to hook and line.

Ma-Kee skirted the gloomy patch of water, passing close to the shoreline to do so. A deep, stump-strewn bay beckoned invitingly but she swam on, heading always in the direction of the current. At twilight great turtles rested in the surface water of the bay, their heads protruding like the butt ends of felled saplings.

On the far side of the lake is another creature that has sensed the current and been attracted toward it. It is Lampetra, the sea lamprey, one of the family of blood-sucking vertebrates which found their way into the Lakeland via Lake Huron after a difficult ten-year pilgrimage from their native Lake Ontario.

As the Great Ice Age terminated and the glaciers gave back water to the sea, an expansion of the Gulf of St Lawrence occurred. Quite likely, Lampetra's forbears entered the Lake Ontario basin at the time of this marine invasion. Not, however, until man began his slow linking of the waterways did they have access to the upper lakes.

Lampetra is the product of the first lampreys to invade the Lakeland.

Far up a shallow stream one spring day the parent lampreys had scooped out hollows in the stream bed and then mated. From this and subsequent matings, thousands of white eggs were deposited and fertilized. The larvae that succeeded in hatching were not long in looking after themselves. Almost immediately, having drifted to a quiet spot, they dug into the mud and there remained for several years, only their heads protruding, devoid of all senses save the one that bade them pump water continuously through their pharynxes, small food particles in the water being extracted and swallowed in the process.

Then came the time when Lampetra developed eyes and his specialized, rasping teeth. His blood-sucking activities began immediately, continuing with increasing vigour for the twelve months (the better part of his adult life) that he remained in the vicinity of the stream.

Now he is more than a foot long, mottled brown in colour to match the sand on which he often lies, and he feels the necessity of larger prey if he is to winter successfully. Like Ma-Kee he is on a scouting trip. But, unlike her, his progress has been in slower stages. For, from time to time, he must anchor to stones and other smooth-surfaced projections with the boneless sucking disc Nature has given him instead of jaws.

This peculiar characteristic earned the lamprey his name: stonesucker. It also betokened an unusual ability to surmount physical obstacles.

Clamped to an obstruction, he could shift position by repeatedly extending the fore part of his rubbery "jaws" so that the area encompassed by his mouth was ovate rather than circular, then drawing up the rear section until the jaw shape was more or less circular once more. He literally "walked" with his mouth. Stones and rocks were negotiated with ease. Scaling the sheer height of a forty-foot dam was a task more difficult only because it was more time-consuming.

It was this faculty that had enabled the parent lampreys to surmount obstacles in their path on the way up the Severn River—in particular the dams at Swift Rapids and Big Chute where marine railways, instead of locks, are used to permit the passage of boats. After a year or so in Lake Simcoe they then wandered into the Lakeland.

The current that both Lampetra and Ma-Kee seek comes from the channel that winds its way down the centre of the lake. This is part of the artery that feeds the lake system, carrying water from the height of land to the west, down through the several lakes in the chain to the river Trent which eventually finds outlet in Lake Ontario.

At each end of the lake are dams, the one funnelling the flow of the upper lakes, the other precipitating the flow to a still lower level. Both are equipped with lift-locks to permit the passage of vessels from one level to another. And the dam at the lower end of the flow has a power plant as well.

Within a mile of the lower dam, Lampetra reaches the channel. Years before, when logging made commerce profitable over much of the lake system, a barge had sunk in the channel. Its timbers rotted, the nails standing out like fangs, it now lies derelict on the bottom. But for all its aura of moss-grown helplessness, it is a welcome sight to Lampetra. Wriggling his serpentine way through the pale green depths he clamps his soft, tooth-lined mouth to the underside of a beam. He is content. Now, let what chances come his way . . .

Ma-Kee, meanwhile, has scoured most of one side of the lake, having had to detour twice more in order to avoid crossing other deep holes between her and the channel.

A bass shoal now lies in her path and she approaches it suspiciously. This is one of several shoals, rising like graveyards out of the lake bottom. Their boulder-strewn lengths are familiar to fishermen, who call them by such names as Bald Point, False Duck, and Cartwright's Shoal, and locate them by means of landmarks on the shore or by patient sounding. Here small-mouth bass congregate, feeding chiefly on crayfish, which abound among the rocks.

Despite her early encounters with Leaper, the small-mouth's deep-chested cousin of the marshes, Ma-Kee no longer fears either of these members of the bass family. But she holds them in respect, knowing them to be valiant fighters when aroused. She begins, therefore, to skirt the shoal, and is well on the way to being successful when suddenly she is among a fleet of fingerlings from that spring's hatch.

Sight of the sleek coppery youngsters, spiny sails set in nautical splendour, overwhelms stomach and craw.

But a defender is on the scene. He is an old, heavy-shouldered bass, bearing the scars of many battles. A rusted hook, the eye end jutting from the tough gristle of his jaw, indicates that fishermen, as well, have met him unsuccessfully in combat.

Rudely, the old bass interposes himself between Ma-Kee and her prospective dinner. His mien is not threatening. He stands guard, like a watchdog, unconcerned but formidable.

Ma-Kee heeds the warning. With a quick tail-thrust she is gone, and has soon departed the shoal. There are other, easier ways of getting a meal.

Presently she brings her gaunt form to a halt again, senses alert. The inclination to extend wide her opercles and expose the blood-red surfaces of her gills receives sudden impetus.

The channel is close by. In minutes more she is at its edge, luxuriating in the gradual but powerful flow. She senses that this is a dividing line bisecting the lake's mysteries. Well, she need go no farther.

Of course, to follow the flow of the channel is a temptation. The distant thunder of the dam is caught up molecularly and translated by her sensitive hearing line. This mystery is one that somehow summons her.

Hesitantly she strikes out, careful to keep a respectful distance from the channel, for instinct tells her that dangers lurk along its edge. Others of her own species, especially very large members, lie almost perpetually in wait at some part of the dark corridor. There, too, on bright days the dark form of Ravenor, the bowfin, lies at a higher level where the weeds camouflage him, his presence unsuspected by all save the most discerning.

At length the rotted hulk of the barge appears below Ma-Kee. It arouses her curiosity and she dives to inspect it.

Settled well down into the murky bottom, the barge had long since ceased to be a menace to the shallow-draught boats that plied the channel. In the half-light, clothed in luminous green, it was a sunken castle. Locks of weed slime streamed from its wooden uprights, and now and then came a gleam, as though of tinsel, as silver-bodied dace slipped in and out through the chinks and cracks in its sides.

Ma-Kee has all but passed the beam where Lampetra hangs

suspended when the stonesucker spies her. With galvanic swiftness, Lampetra looses his hold and launches himself toward her.

The impact staggers Ma-Kee. The lamprey has attached himself to her chest, and almost at once his hundred sawteeth and spear-tipped tongue rasp at the circular area of scales encompassed by his fringed lips.

Lampetra has been well designed. Of an order of aquatic animals old in the history of the earth, every detail of his body lends itself to his gruesome work.

In a way, he is superior to the true fishes, for he does not need to take water into his mouth in order to breathe. This important function is performed by a series of vents on either side of his head. Through these openings, which are connected with the gill chambers, he can both inhale and exhale, independent of all else. It is a handy arrangement indeed, in a world where opening one's mouth even for an instant can mean the escape of one's prey.

What a threshing and twisting and turning now goes on in the depth! Ma-Kee has no way of knowing what manner of creature has attacked her. Its weight is not great and, occasionally, in her first frenzied attempts to shake off her attacker, she glimpses a body hardly larger around than a lily-pad stalk. But the cruel buzz-saw rasping on her underside leaves no doubt that it is something to be feared.

Like a dog trying to free itself of a dragging rope, she sounds and rubs her belly against the bottom. To no avail. Lampetra's fleshy lips, pressed flat against her, and the exudation of water through his vents, have created a partial vacuum. Even Ma-Kee's slippery coating of body slime does not help. The lamprey's hold remains firm.

Now Ma-Kee tries rushing through the water at breakneck speed, the current lending her momentum. Yet, after a while, she finds her unwelcome burden still with her, and she slows down.

The dam is now a thundering sound. The vibration causes her microscopic sound-chambers to throb so that her sides ache. And Lampetra, by now, has chopped through the scale layer and is feasting on her blood and juices.

Out of the current! Away from the terrifying roar!

With all her might she strives to obey these impulses. But she cannot. In her weakened condition the pressure of water is too great. And looming before her is the intake pipe, through which water is channelled to the turbines below.

Collision with the iron grating that screens the intake is inevitable. Fortunately, the smashing contact is insufficient to kill or maim; it only stuns.

Lampetra cushions the blow as, together, they strike the grating. Ma-Kee is drawn flat, momentarily transfixed. But now there is additional pull on her body. For the lamprey, smaller in circumference than the openings in the screen, is suddenly sucked in, tail first.

Faced with this unexpected dénouement, Lampetra lets go and is washed to his destruction. Ma-Kee, relieved of the burden, slithers and wriggles her way clear of the grating and in a moment is out of the path of the current. A short distance more and she is safe in the tranquil sidewaters of the dam.

A raw wound shows on her chest. In time a new coating of scales will cover it over. But the mark will never entirely disappear.

Weir Pool

DESPITE her weakened condition, Ma-Kee could not content herself to remain long in the unexpected haven into which she had been delivered.

The roar of the dam seemed to crowd down upon her, engulfing her, pressing its tumult of sound deep into her brain. It was not enough to be free of her strange assailant. She must also be free of this additional terror.

Feebly, calling on what little strength she had left, she headed back up the lake. In time, the roar became a murmur, finally dying out altogether. When she could hear it no longer she availed herself of the first satisfactory shelter and gave herself up to rest.

After some days she felt much better. The wound left by Lampetra's rasp-like teeth was partially healed. Hunger drove her to feed again, reviving her energy. She had a new lease on life, and was ready to make the most of it.

As a result of her experience at the power dam, the channel now lay between her and the side of the lake from which she had come. To avoid facing the dangers of the mysterious corridor once again, she must continue on up the lake, following the flow toward its source. At some point, perhaps, the crossing would be less hazardous.

But such was not to be the case. The channel ran on for several miles, terminating at the dam that marked the next step up in the lake system. Once reaching here, she will have to turn back, whether she crosses the channel or not . . .

The dam at this end of the lake is of no great height, having been erected on the site of a shallow rapids. Because of the dry weather, only one sluice is open. From the iron jaws a sparse flow courses softly down over the face of the connecting chute. The remaining chutes, lacking even this modicum of moisture, stand parched and forlorn, their rough cement surfaces yellowed by decaying algae.

To one side of the dam is the lift lock that serves to bridge the gap between the upper and lower lakes. At its base, a pleasure boat lies at anchor. It is on its way to Georgian Bay in the last stages of a late-season trip through the waters of the Lakeland. In the pleasant Indian summer sunshine the occupants recline in various attitudes of ease on deck and gunwales and in canvas-backed chairs, talking and admiring the scenery while awaiting the opening of the heavy ribbed gates.

Into the comparative quiet of the lock approach swims Ma-Kee, having taken to the shoreline some while back in preference to the channel margin. She makes her way cautiously, ready to flee. For the deep rock bowl in which she finds herself is not to her liking and she senses the same unnatural set of conditions that climaxed her adventure with Lampetra.

Stay! Here is a familiar note. Overhead, resting at ease, is a large boat. A queer kind of reassurance. Yet it serves to allay her apprehensions simply by its presence.

And now the gates part at the mitre post. In unison, the boat's engine starts up, its throaty cough sending a stab of alarm through the muskellunge. A shaft of light pierces the gloom ahead of her. In a trice she is off, bolting with arrow swiftness through the chamber opening. This way, perhaps, lies safety.

Consternation fills her a moment later. In her hurry to get away she has run into a stone. In a panic she turns in another direction. Again she rams her snout painfully against the stone. Confused, she noses along the far gate like a minnow in an aquarium. To no avail. The barrier is impenetrable. She is trapped.

Now she is in for another fright. For the boat has followed her. It moves heavily, whipping the water to foam with its tail, the noise of its progress welling into a fearful sound within the enclosure, and she unable to flee. Then, as she feels the noise overwhelming her, it ceases, and the boat comes to rest above her.

The gates close, shutting out the light. Water pours in through the sluices.

Deep in one corner of the chamber, Ma-Kee suffers this new menace with a calm that is forced upon her by reason of her helplessness. The water tumbles around her, buffeting her like wind gusts, now thrusting her from side to side, now sweeping her completely around. Grimly, each time, she regains her balance, only to be forced to renew her stubborn resistance once again.

She is in a veritable cauldron.

Gradually, as the chamber fills, the agitation is lessened. Now the sluices close. The upper level has been reached. Above, set in motion by the lock-keeper, the balance beams controlling the gates go into action.

The sudden movement of the strange impenetrable barrier causes Ma-Kee to wheel about and dart to the rear of the chamber.

Once more the coughing roar of the boat reverberates through the enclosure, subsiding before long in a loud moan. The noise all but paralyses her. But she sees suddenly what the boat must have seen : light. Not merely a thin shaft such as had led them into this trap, but a whole wide volume of light, beckoning, luminous, hope-stirring.

Silver clouds of bubbles rise about the boat's stern. It is moving, escaping, out into the freedom of the light. She must follow.

She seizes on the opportunity, rushing forward in the wake of the huge surface creature whose enforced companion she had been for so many agonizing moments. Now she is past the lock. But the dazzling brilliance of the outside world and the churned-up water blinds and confuses her.

Before she is aware of the danger, she is under the boat's whirling tail. Too late, she veers off. The metal blade catches her a glancing blow. A darkness, greater by far than the gloom of the lock chamber, descends upon her.

And now the cruiser rises up out of the bowels of the lock and enters the lake. Before breasting the inviting waters in earnest, its engines idle. For the lock-keeper, a rotund ruddy-faced man in blue pants and neat striped shirt, has advanced to the dam edge to say a word of greeting.

At this point Ma-Kee, half floating, half lifted by the upward push of water in the area of the boat's screw, comes to the surface. There she lies, long and resplendent of form, a red gash showing behind her gill cover.

A shout arises from the boat. "Look! A muskie!"

"It's hurt!" another voice exclaims excitedly.

The lock-keeper, from his position on the dam, squints, then shields his eyes to get a better look.

"Sure enough," he remarks, as though half-doubting his eyes. "Probably hit by the propeller." He trundles off, waving a cautioning arm. "Wait. I'll get a pike pole."

There is a pike pole in the cruiser, too, and the most excited of the passengers manages to get it free of chairs and other impedimenta and, wielding it like a spear to the imminent danger of his fellows, clambers out onto the stern where he several times flops the far end into the water near the fish.

His reach is short, however, which gives the returning lock-keeper his chance. Hastily, envisioning a tasty meal, he squats on the edge of the dam wall and, with difficulty, extends the pole.

Alas. His reach, too, is short.

"Put the motor in reverse," someone in the boat now suggests. There is laughter, for the whole affair has become a game. But the suggestion is taken seriously and in a moment the motor whines and the boat slowly begins to back water.

Not to be outdone, the lock-keeper makes a final awkward effort, stretching body and arm to the limit. The try is ill-fated. His pudgy form is not designed for fine balance. Off the wall he goes with a splash.

"Look out!" But the warning is too late. A woman's scream follows, transforming apprehension into shocked realization.

Fortunately, the boat is backing in the right direction. The pike pole is now put to more efficient use and the lock-keeper is soon fished out, wet and gasping.

Unnoticed in the excitement, Ma-Kee recovers her senses and slowly swims off. She is free. Limitless space abounds. A sudden feeling of exhilaration sends her forward through the water with new strength.

The lake in which Ma-Kee now found herself had a second outlet, located at the end of a slender bay some distance above the dam. Here a waste weir had been erected, limiting the escape of water to flood periods. At such times, the water spurted through the notched sluices in terrifying volume, cascading down a slowly declining rock slope into the valley below and eventually finding entrance to the lower lake. But not all the flow was dissipated in this fashion. In many years of swollen, ice-laden freshets, an entrance had been gained to the low-lying terrain at one side of the weir, creating a backwater.

Weir Pool it was called. For though it was large and, in parts, deep, it was circular in shape. And its surface, protected from the wind by the surrounding woodland, was almost always calm and glossy.

Never quite succumbing to summer drought, replenished by rains and by succeeding freshets, the pool remained a permanent part of the lake scene. In time, trees had rotted and fallen. Seeds of water plants, washed in from the lake, had found fertile footing in the rich loam floor and provided weed cover. In summer, duckweed and frog spittle usurped almost its entire surface, while in the bog areas from which the water had retreated red-veined pitcher plants reared from beds of pale sphagnum moss.

Occasionally, of an early summer evening, a boat would cross the shallow bar at the entrance and nose cautiously into the pool. A fisherman would rise to his feet and make a cast in among the stumps, as often as not being rewarded by the catapulting strike of a bass. Once in a while the answering swirl would be more explosive. The fisherman's line would race, and he would grow tense. A muskie!

But if the first few casts brought no result he would give up and retreat to the lake. He knew that the fish had been put down and that further effort was useless.

Several small perch are idling at the pool mouth. Not far away, a rapidly mouldering growth of shore weed takes on a suspiciously darker hue.

Should they investigate? Their barely formed sense of caution warns them not to. Fortunate, indeed, their decision. For of a sudden they are scurrying in terror across the now almost exposed bar separating them from the shelter of the pool, a demon hurtling after them.

With jaws half open for the kill, Ma-Kee strikes the soft sand of the bar with her underside. It throws her off stride and she reaches the deeper water of the pool with a struggle, all the while scowling. For her intended victims have made good their escape. Useless, she knows, to attempt to find them in the mass of roots and vegetation that now greets her.

Several days in the lake have seen her rapidly on the mend. She is ravenous and cannot seem to get enough to eat. Ordinarily she would not travel so far without holing up. But the brisk temperature of late autumn has spurred her on. Besides, food is scarce. It must be sought.

She noses forward, expressionless eyes alert. The perch are gone. But other less wary morsels may await her jaws. Eel grass blades bend to the touch of a fin. Some, under the weight of her body, break and partly crumble, loosing a rain of powdery particles. Every rotted tree branch disturbed by her passage gives off a shower of algae.

The scuttling movement of a crayfish brings alarm. Away

she shoots, bringing up at a distance where a thick inter-
twined mass of elodea lies like a pile of rusted chain. Behind
her she has left a smoky path in which water lice and boat-
bugs dart excitedly.

This is only one of numerous bog-masses, separated cleanly
by deep areas in which no growth has taken hold. As she
emerges from the first, a large sunfish sails giddily ahead of
her. She is on top of it almost before either is aware of the
other's presence, seizing it with a rapacious thrust and gulping it straight down into her craw.

In the next clearing a perch falls to her attack. Then, with
a spring, she is on the trail of a milky-grey fish that launches
into ghostly flight from its bed of bottom muck. Her speed
soon narrows the gap, and the sucker is caught as though in
a nail-studded press.

Fortune has smiled on her. The pool is like a well-stocked
larder.

But after a week her steady rounds of the pool have gone

far toward depleting it. The potential victims of any size that are left, have taken to remaining in the shelter of the weeds. Intuition dictates that she seek new hunting grounds.

She heads for the pool entrance. But it somehow is not where it was before, and she ranges back and forth in the general area until the truth becomes clear. The sand bar is high and dry. She is shut in!

No alternative presents itself but to return to the bog-holes and make the best of things. This she does, selecting a hiding place at the edge of the deepest hole and accommodating herself to her change of fortunes.

The nights now become colder. One morning, a chickadee which has been accustomed to drink daintily from the pool edge, finds to its dismay that the water has acquired an odd hardness.

Fluttering and slipping out over the glittering surface it comes at last to where the ice ends. There, for a breath-taking instant, it almost drowns. Ma-Kee, watching with interest, rushes to the spot. It is her sudden-looming appearance that saves the little grey-black bird which, with a frightened *ka-dee-ee*, at last flies to the safety of the bush.

Now begins a reign of terror for the creatures still remaining in the pool. No thing is safe from the gaunt fury in their midst. Minnows, shiners, suckers, one by one disappear. Hunger even overcomes Ma-Kee's aversion to catfish. She learns to gorge them by degrees, stoically ignoring the stinging pain, inflicted even in death, of their fin spikes.

Her craft grows greater as her quarry's numbers dwindle. For hours she will lie, so kindred in appearance to stump or log as to defy detection. A jay, spying her dark shape on such an occasion, leaves its tree branch and hovers screaming over the water, only to fly off before long, perhaps convinced that it is mistaken.

She turns to nosing in the mud for snails. And once, by accident, she unearths a frog. Hope rises within her as the squirming green shape shoots off across the bottom, frantically employing muscular legs to propel it out of the danger area. So startled is she that she does not follow. But she will remember. Here, perhaps, is a fresh source of sustenance.

On a day not long after, as she lies in her narrow bog-hole nursing her hunger, she is startled to see a slim, furry form emerge from among the plantain roots. Its front paws dig and tear at the bottom. A flash of green, evidently the reward that has been expected, and a frog bursts into sight ahead of the curious invader. Immediately it is seized in sharp teeth. Keen eyes, dominating a pointed, kitten face, glance in Ma-Kee's direction. Then the furry body rises up out of her domain into the world above.

The whole affair has lasted only seconds. But it portends no good. There is little enough food for one. To learn that she must share that little with another is too much. In reckless hunting mood she storms through the pool.

Food! It is a refrain that every part of her knows by heart. But her wild excursion is fruitless. The few sunfish and perch that have so far escaped with their lives are warned afar of her coming. Crayfish dig farther in under logs. Leeches flatten themselves against the most convenient obstructions.

When her rage is dissipated Ma-Kee sinks morosely to rest. For a full day she does not move.

Meanwhile, the mink—for such it was—goes about his activities unconcerned. Time after time he visits the pool. And almost always he emerges with a dinner—if not a frog, a fish.

He is a newcomer to the district. The fishing in the pool does not wholly satisfy him. But, combined with hunting excursions along the shore, it will serve until winter drives him to his den.

A night in November sees him abroad. A full moon soars in lofty splendour. It is his favourite hunting time. Tracking soft-footed over the forest fringe, he scents a field mouse. Sinuous body hugging the ground, he creeps close for a leap, and a frightened little squeak becomes a death cry. But alas, no more mice are to be found.

The mink now turns his attentions to the pool. There is some kind of large grey fish that frequents the deepest boghole. Now, there would be prey worth catching!

Quivering with excitement, he enters the water. Rapidly, through one hole after another, he goes, all the while making ready his attack. He will simply come up under the sleeping fish. A slash of his jaws and it will be over.

He is so thinking when one leg and hind quarter are seized in a painful grip.

Ma-Kee is not in her usual hole. She has taken to haunting each of the holes in turn, hoping to catch the animal intruder off guard. Suddenly, limned against the moon-bright sky, the mink's sinuous form rides into view above her. Up, through the yielding darkness! . . . Up, until teeth at last meet their objective!

The pain and terror of being thus unexpectedly attacked precipitates a wild attempt by the mink to break free. But the powerful grip on his leg does not lessen. Worse, he is slowly being dragged backwards beneath the surface.

He must do battle or die. With this fact made clear, all his animal cunning comes to his aid. Ceasing to resist, he draws in a last lungful of air, then, in a lightning move, doubles under the muskellunge, throwing Ma-Kee off balance with the sudden shifting of his weight. At the same time he uses his front feet to slash at her belly.

This move, coupled with Ma-Kee's efforts to lift her body beyond the slashing claws, sets them to tumbling over and over, now one on top, now the other. The strain of maintaining such an awkward position soon tells on the mink, and he is forced to try new tactics.

Now his front feet find purchase on an underwater branch. In the ensuing tug-of-war, Ma-Kee's hold slips. She now has only the mink's foot in her jaws.

At once, the mink realizes his disadvantage has lessened. Whirling, he fastens his teeth in his opponent's back.

The tables are turned. To cope with this new state of affairs Ma-Kee must release her hold entirely.

Furiously she races the length of the hole, the mink swinging behind, clinging like a ferret to a rabbit. Unseen obstructions claw and pull at him, but at the end of the rush he remains fast.

Striking shallow ground, Ma-Kee does her best to dislodge the slim furry creature by manoeuvring it against the bottom. Without success. The effort is too much for her already weakened condition and at length she calls a halt. Her whole body trembles. Now she feels in full earnest the pain of the mink's teeth.

The mink takes advantage of the lull to sink his teeth deeper. He is taken aback at his adversary's show of strength. He is discomfited, too, by having to remain under water for such a length of time. If the battle lasts much longer he will have to let go.

Now Ma-Kee is away again, racing into the blackness. Seldom has the usually placid pool seen such a commotion. Waves like liquid metal flee across the surface. Bits of wood and decayed vegetation rise everywhere, blotting out small sections of sky wherever they come to rest.

Now again Ma-Kee slows down, and the mink, in a last weakened effort, tries to draw her surfaceward. But she is too heavy. Even if she had no fight left in her, he could not accomplish the task.

His lungs cry out for air. He must let go!

To make good his escape he is forced to expose himself once more to the jaws of his opponent. A moment later his worst fears are realized. He again feels himself seized, this time about the middle.

Happily, he has lost consciousness when, in the darkness, Ma-Kee begins the formidable task of gorging her vanquished foe.

The mink lasted Ma-Kee several weeks. By that time, winter was well advanced. The ice became thicker, until all but the deepest holes were solid to the bottom.

Then, in February, an early thaw set in. One awful night the ice far up the lake gave way and a wall of water, bearing ice chunks the size of sidewalk blocks, swept down upon the weir.

Amid ear-splitting chaos it invaded the pool, breaking up the ice and setting the water free.

Ma-Kee, caught up in the torrent, was carried with it over the weir into the valley below. Bruised, but alive, she eventually felt the cushioned impact of quiet water. Her fins, she found, would support her body. Without haste she departed the open water of the river mouth, moving far out under the comforting shelter of the shadow.

She was back in her own lake.

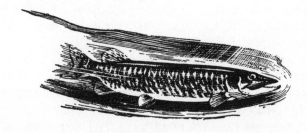

The Pickerel Run

A BOY, tossing stones into the water in the river channel near the dam, was the first to see the gathering of fish.

Standing balanced on the balls of his feet like a boxer, one arm raised in the act of throwing, he froze, breath and all, in a moment of suspended movement, arrested by the sight of sudden-looming fish shapes where there had been but murky water before.

What were they? *What were they?*

The stone-tossing now was forgotten. Tensely he lowered his arm—body, head, and eyes compacted into an eager, watchful unit, like a heron readying itself to strike.

More shapes came into view, then others. They appeared to move in clusters, forging steadily up-river. And because the ones he could see swam close to shore instead of keeping to the deeper water in the middle, he sensed that they were crowded there by main ranks of fish, farther out.

What were they?

At last his opportunity came. For now several fish passed close over a limestone slab jutting palely under water from the base of the rocky bank, and their distinguishing marks showed more plainly.

Suckers? No, there would be no mistaking the rounded whitish fins, the blunt head.

Pickerel? The ice had been out only a week and they were not expected yet. Besides, the smoky-eyed invaders had never before been seen in such numbers in the lower lakes. But he had fished with his father many times and knew the look of a pickerel on a stringer.

Ecstatically, the truth flashed upon him. In another moment he was bounding up the bank with the news. They were pickerel, without a doubt. *The run was on!*

The storekeeper in the village, dispenser also of choice pieces of local information, was next to know. Then the gas station attendant at the corner, which the hurrying youngster rounded at a gallop on his way home. Then his father, who received the news with just the right amount of adult interest and, a minute after, to make it plain that the momentousness of the occasion was not lost upon him, admonished the boy with a sudden smile to "Git then, and rassle up some bait!"

It spread quickly after that. By dark, there were few in the village who did not know.

To Ame Russell in his shack down by the lake it came like a wind of good fortune, warming him through as the thin spring sunshine had failed to do and setting him to working over lines and rods and sundry other equipment against the time—probably the following evening if the wind held right—when the fishing would begin.

Big, slow-moving, uncommunicative, renowned for his feats with rod and gun, Old Ame had the peculiar distinction of being a legend in the district while he remained very much alive. In his younger days he had logged and trapped. Now in his declining years he lived on the precarious edge of comfort, sustained, but for a few purchased necessities, by the products of his vegetable patch and the uncertain spoils of woods and water. It was common belief (rather more than a suspicion) that he availed himself of the latter as he required them, without respect for fish and game laws.

In proper season, from spring to late fall, his bamboo pole took constant toll of available species of fish. He included in his take even the smaller panfish, such as rock bass and perch —sometimes for the sake of variety, often because their larger cousins failed to respond even to his special brand of skill.

"Suckerin'," following the spring break-up, was a highly productive food source. Catches were invariably large. And when he had satisfied his immediate needs, what remained of the fleshy fish chunks he brined or smoked for later consumption.

The hunting season provided him with additional opportunities to supply his table legitimately. But even the wiliest and most energetic of meat hunters would have been hard put to live off the land twelve months of the year without digressing from the rules. All manner of accusations, broadly spoken or darkly hinted at, were therefore laid at Ame's door.

It was rumoured, for instance, that jacking deer at night in their winter yards was a standard method of adding to his meat supply; that wire snares produced many a plump partridge for his stewpot; and that if one were to journey to certain remote lakes when the ice was on, there Old Ame would often be spied crouched over a hole, effectively manoeuvring spear and decoy to bring about the end of many a fat lake trout. Once a gill net was discovered set downriver from Ame's shack. But the most prolonged questioning by Moses Todd, the Game Warden, failed to bring about an admission of guilt.

Through all this, winter and summer, his huge bulk, from waist to shoulders like a tightly drawn sack of flour, sustained in solid good health by the proceeds of his skill, and with a mocking smile reserved specially for the Warden, Old Ame went his solitary way. He was a relic of a dying profession, a poacher of the old school. The locals recognized this and, in the main, shrugged tolerantly.

"Anyone who can get away with it as long as Old Ame has," they philosophized, "deserves to."

They meant, by inference, that he was lucky to get away with it with "Holy" Moses Todd at his heels. Not that the Warden hadn't done his best to apprehend his will-o'-the-wisp quarry. He would have reproached himself bitterly had he not. But his territory was wide, and Old Ame was slippery.

The Warden's nickname was well earned. Moses Todd pursued his calling like an avenging angel and had never been known to take a bribe.

Deceptively slight (law-breakers had felt the sinewy strength of his grasp), he had an incurable squint, due, no doubt, to long hours of spying from awkward positions in alder thicket and rice screen.

During the course of his duties he had been fired at, set upon, threatened, left stranded when his boat was stolen; suffered altogether innumerable affronts and inconveniences. Once, after dark, poachers had tricked him to the shore of the lake below a rock crest and had dumped boulders onto him from above. He wore bandages for months after, but never gave up the chase. A charge of buckshot from some unknown source had left him permanently lame.

His continued hostilities with Old Ame weighed on him. In his heart he had a soft spot for the old man. "What a warden he would have made!" he often thought. But Old Ame was a poacher, and one day would have to pay the penalty.

Thus it was that when the Warden, at his home twenty miles distant, got the announcement of the pickerel run (the mailman, returning from his rural-route deliveries, had deemed it judicious to pass the word along), a picture of Old Ame making ready his tackle flashed across his mind. The temptation would be great, while the run was on, to take more than the legal limit.

"The old rascal's about due to make a false step," he ruminated with a flicker of a smile. Well, he would be on hand to trip him up if he did.

Before many months had passed following her latest misadventure, Ma-Kee had forgotten the perils of the dam and was roaming the lake freely once more. Restrictions of any kind were at odds with her constantly waxing size and strength. She must have space aplenty in which to move.

There was an additional reason for her need to roam freely.

The pickerel were now present in such numbers that they had become serious competitors for the perch and suckers and other such forage fish on which she fed. True, she often took advantage of the situation and fed on them. But their spiny dorsals were not to her liking. And besides, the golden-scaled newcomers travelled in packs for protection. It was not easy to pounce on young fish without inviting trouble, for many formidable old fish travelled with them.

When she had little luck foraging in her accustomed manner, which happened not infrequently now, she took to following the pickerel packs. Eventually this led to food, for the pickerel were good hunters. If the booty was minnows, she waited until they had been herded into position, then joined in the attack; if some less manageable quarry, she stayed behind, hopeful of victims that by luck or adroitness managed to escape the marauders and emerged from the safety of the weeds at their passing.

Thus it was that one May evening Ma-Kee found herself entering the river channel that led to the upper dam. The company of pickerel she had been following had not led her to food as she had expected. And soon, to her bewilderment, other packs joined the first, flocking in from all directions.

Caught in the press of fish, she moved with them. Unaware that she was attending the nuptial ceremonies of her arch-rivals, she stayed—an uninvited guest.

"The run is on!" It was a heart-warming, spirit-lifting message. Wherever it was heard it brought exclamations of "Is that so!" and "Well, ain't that something!" For it aroused visions of excitement-filled nights and flopping fish and animated talk; of fishing gear rescued from winter's disuse and readied for action; of the first bracing salute to a new season.

The run was a matter of considerable magnitude in other ways. To many, like Ame Russell, it meant food. To the business people in the village it meant fishermen from outside points, sales of cigarettes and candy and gasoline, rooms in hotel and tourist homes filled. It meant a brisk week or so's business for bait-sellers who netted chub in nearby streams. It meant, as it had in the upper lakes where the pickerel were first planted, additional publicity for the village as a fishing spot and the return, year after year, of many of the fishermen who came for the event.

"The run is on!"

As though carried by the wind, but in reality relayed by many mouths, and by telephone and telegraph, the news travelled overnight to farmhouse, to village, to town and city. By suppertime the next day they began arriving, drawn to the river channel with its wide concrete dam by almost as sure a pull as that obeyed by the swarming fish; boys of grade-school age, determined to snatch a few hours' fun before darkness summoned them home, but none too hopeful, knowing that the night fishing was the most productive; old cronies exuberant with the renewal of comradeship; experts bent on selecting the best locations while it was still light; amateurs beset by uncertainty, fumbling with tackle, casting inquiring glances at the rigs and baits of others, excited, impatient. Those who had thrown their gear together hastily had cause to regret it. Those who had neglected to bring extra clothing shivered in the chill spring air and vowed to remember next time.

Positions were taken first over the sluices through which the water roared and curled and then sprawled out in bulging green ribbons that raced away downstream. Gradually other vantage points were filled. And occasionally fishermen, unwilling to be restricted to the shallow side-eddies, took to the rocky banks that formed the shoreline.

As the night advanced, car headlights in the field on the one approachable side of the dam blinked on and off like huge fireflies. And in the distance glimmers as though of lightning soon became searching animated shafts as still other cars found the road and then, in sudden blazing intensity, the field.

On the dam, now crowded, lighted feebly by lofty lamp standards at either end, tension mounted. Fishermen talked of baits, of moon, of wind, of weather, of big fish, restlessly peered at the vague figures stretching into infinity on either side for signs of activity, endlessly inspected and re-inspected hooks and lines and baits by means of flashlights which, each time, they replaced gingerly beside them. "What's happening? Is anyone catching anything?" they asked over and over. "Wonder if they'll bite? Maybe it's too early yet."

Like the strings on a tilted harp, awaiting the strumming that only hungry fish-mouths could give them, the lines stretched taut from dam to water. Then came word that two pickerel had been taken somewhere down the long line of waiting fishermen. Someone nearby gave a quick strike, reeled furiously, then, grasping the line, hauled up hand over hand what was unmistakably a fish. A four-pounder, at least.

At last, fulfilment. They were beginning to hit.

Along the bank opposite the field, partly camouflaged by a cluster of dwarf willows, a hulking figure bit on his pipe and stared out at the water.

Old Ame, in dungarees and thick wool sweater, had lifted his pole many times since he had arrived early in the evening. But in the water in front of him, in a mesh bag tethered by its draw strings to the jutting finger of a log, was only one pickerel. For Ame, who fished fine and usually got quick results, the showing was poor. In his stubbly countenance, however, was nothing to betray disappointment.

His bamboo pole was of a length that permitted him, when required, to swing his bait easily into difficult spots. Often it was his practice simply to tie a length of line to the tip, relying on its stoutness to subdue his catch without give and take. For the business at hand, it was fitted with guides and a reel well filled with fine silk casting line.

Pickerel were shy biters. The approach, particularly in the daylight, must be delicate. At the same time it was necessary to compensate for the lighter line; hence the reel.

Ignoring the activity on the dam, Old Ame kept a sharp eye on his line which, bearing its tempting chub-burden, was continually at the mercy of the currents and had to be watched lest it be swept shoreward or tangle with other lines. The last was an ever present threat. Every few minutes, it seemed, someone was hauling in someone else's line together with his own. A shout would arise from the offended party. Flashlights would blink and waver as figures huddled together, heads bent, hands seeking to clear the tangle.

As his painstakingly seductive methods called for, from time to time Old Ame retrieved line in halting movements, then, lifting his pole high in order to guide the bait into favourable water, allowed the line to run out swiftly.

Mid way in one such manoeuvre he had the sensation that a fish had taken the bait. But as it was during the run-out of the line, he could not be sure.

Cautiously he braked the line by letting the palm of his hand touch the reel handle. Now he felt the drag distinctly. But, being well practised in the art of giving a fish line, he immediately removed the pressure from the reel. Let it run. In a moment it would stop and commence to swallow the bait. Then he could strike.

Only when he saw danger in the diminishing spool did he do so. By the solid feel as the hook set, he knew he was into a heavy fish.

Now the fish moved toward him. It was in a backwash and there was no pull of water to give him trouble. He reeled quickly, keeping the line taut. At the same time, perhaps feeling that all was not well, the fish leaped.

Ame bit harder on his pipe. A muskie! White-bellied, shimmering. Gill covers distended like fledgling wings. And, as he had suspected, a good size.

Cautiously he glanced around. No one was near. Down-river where he was, it was dark. From the dam, against the background of restless white water, the fish could hardly have been seen.

He gave slack and settled on his haunches, prepared to wait. Not a frequenter of currents, like pickerel, the muskie would likely confine its struggles to the backwash and thus ease his task. In ten minutes, twenty minutes, perhaps, when it had fought itself out, he could float the fish belly-up down past the willows where it could be beached and, with the aid of his knife, quickly reduced to fillets. The season for muskies was two months away. He would have to be careful.

While Old Ame was thus engaged, a figure appeared against the sky at the top of the rise and stood silently looking down at the lone fisherman. When the figure moved at last and commenced a half slithering, half picked-out descent of the rough slope, the sound reached Ame above the din of the water.

Turning his head he recognized the dim outline of Holy Moses Todd. His glance lasted only long enough to make sure. Then, with slow deliberateness, he turned his attention again to the water.

In a moment or two the Warden was on level ground. He came and sat on the log where it sprawled a few feet from Ame, stretching out his bad leg, simultaneously slapping away a smear of clay from the trouser.

"Evening, Ame," he said after a bit. "How're they biting?"

With no hint that he had heard, Ame stolidly maintained his position, looking fixedly in the direction of his line.

A smile tugged at the Warden's lip ends. The old fellow was determined to ignore him. But it wouldn't be difficult to get an answer to his question. The mesh keep was just a few feet from him, revealed by the drawstring tie.

Using the log for purchase, he drew himself along until, half standing, half leaning, he was able to look down on the keep lying like a clump of decayed seaweed in the still water of the channel's rim.

"One!" Holy Moses's voice showed as much doubt as surprise. He squinted hard at the collapsed folds of the bag with its single dark ridge. He had hoped that Ame had done well —overly well for his own good. He had checked several limit catches on the dam and knew the pickerel were biting. Was the old fellow losing his touch?

With the thought, which he quickly dismissed, came another. Covertly he scanned the area around Ame's squatted hulk. It would be like him to skin out his catch between runs, taking only the two strips of meat, skin included, on either side of the backbone, and thus hide evidence of his success. Seeing no signs, he was disappointed. This wasn't his chance to get the goods on Old Ame after all. The old fellow had probably started late. In a couple of hours—less, perhaps, if the fishing was steady—the mesh bag would present a much different picture.

The Warden yawned and straightened up. His watch showed long after midnight. By the time two hours were up, he'd be in bed. Besides, there would be plenty of other chances to check on Old Ame.

Suddenly his attention was drawn to Ame's rod tip which, despite the latter's efforts to prevent it, was forming an increasingly pronounced arc. True to Old Ame's figuring, Ma-Kee had avoided the main flow. But instinct had bade her nose up-stream on its fringe, slowing her course, and enabling her captor to carry on the fight simply by feeding line.

Nearing the end of his line, however, Ame had been forced to snub the fish in an attempt to turn it. In doing so, his secret was revealed.

" 'Pears you've got a fish on there," said the Warden, staring.

He continued to watch as Ame, successful in checking Ma-Kee's run, leisurely began to retrieve line. The fish could get off, Old Ame knew, with such casual tactics. But he would have to return it anyway, with the Warden there. The thing would be to delay landing it as long as he could. In the meantime perhaps Holy Moses would lose interest and depart.

Now Ma-Kee sortied down-river. Ame gave line as before but, because of the danger of the current, kept a firm pressure on the reel spool. Controlling the fish was easier now.

Returning in a wide swing, Ma-Kee waged her fight in a more confined area. She was still strong, though. And even had he wanted to, Old Ame would not have tried to end the battle at this juncture. But to the Warden, unaware of the size of the prize, it looked like a lost opportunity.

"Well, bring it in, man! Bring it in!" he exclaimed. Then,

conjuring up a joke at Ame's expense: "Season's open. Or didn't you know?"

Stung into replying, Ame removed his now cold pipe from his mouth and, in a quick movement, stuffed it, ashes and all, in his pocket. "A man don't have to swallow one of them rule books to know a simple thing like that." He spat disdainfully. "Besides, I ain't due nowheres. Got a chub on big enough fer a horse. Let him gorge it good an' proper."

"Mighty strange, all that patience." Holy Moses was enjoying himself. "Figured you always fished with a skillet in one hand." Then, as Ma-Kee took a sudden rush shoreward, "Better hang onto that pole before he swallows that, too."

"Mind your business!" exclaimed Old Ame heatedly. He rapidly took in line, careful not to encourage the fish to leap. But the nearness of the action brought Ma-Kee surfaceward. Sensing new danger, she was away again in a powerful swirl.

"Say—that's a good fish!" Holy Moses stared open-mouthed at the spot where the black, heavy-backed shape had appeared. "Get busy, man! That's a record-breaker if I ever saw one."

"No hurry." Ame yawned. Now it was his turn to enjoy the situation. He chuckled inwardly. Let Holy Moses figure this one out.

But he was anxious nevertheless. The whole affair was rapidly reaching a climax. He would have to land the muskie soon. His only chance was to tire the Warden out first—but there seemed little hope of that.

The climax came. But not in the way Ame expected.

On the dam, the line of fishermen had thinned out. Over the sluices, however, there was still an intent cluster, alternately retrieving and paying out line. Glistening like spider's mooring strands, the lines probed the turbulent stretches to the extent that length would permit.

So far, Old Ame had been able to keep free of entanglement. But now Ma-Kee, in her furious rush out of the danger zone, crossed the path of one of the lines.

A shout from the dam indicated that the owner of the line

had felt the shock. Thinking it a strike, he instantly retrieved. The two lines tangled. Before long another fisherman was part of the mix-up and, with two lines being retrieved against him, Ame was forced to give way.

One line had a pickerel on it, and the fisherman was lucky to get it to a point where he could reach it before Ma-Kee came into view.

Far too heavy to be lifted the height of the dam, the strain broke Ame's line and she was free. Both fishermen on the dam let out a groan, for they thought she was a monster pickerel, and there was an ensuing uproar as other fishermen hastily rested their rods and hurried to the spot to hear the excited versions of what had happened.

Down the bank, Ame reeled in his now slack line. His disappointment at losing the muskellunge was overshadowed by his accidental triumph over his long-standing enemy.

"Well, I declare!" he protested indignantly. "Took my pickerel right off, that feller did! You seen him."

Some time later, when the sound of the Warden's car came to his ears, he walked to a crevice in the rocks below the willow clump.

Reaching down, he partially lifted a string of flopping pickerel.

"Three more than the limit," he said softly. "Not bad for a start."

Trapped!

YEARS go by and Ma-Kee grows into a fine specimen of her kind. She now weighs upward of twenty pounds. She is longer by a foot, deeper, and thicker through. If caught by an angler of average height and held suspended, head at his hip, her tail would drag the ground. Two handspreads would just encircle her.

Gone is the snake look that, through much of her early life, made her seem one continuous length from snout to tail. Her body is now her dominant feature, its handspan depth quite dwarfing the scowling jaws and head that spear point its progress. Her back, from above, looks like a length of railroad track. Her tail is as broad as an oar blade.

She is a terrifying sight at the moment of attack. For, although her head now looks a mere implement willed to do the bidding of her body, it is even more appalling in its various aspects than before.

Escape those parted jaws, looming ever nearer? Not likely. Looking into them is like looking into a cavern. Even her stalactite-stalagmite collection of teeth abets this illusion.

A regular ridge of muscle on her nape conjoins with distended opercles to appear like an enormous ruff. And, more than ever, her eyes seem the work of some unholy taxidermy. Perched batrachian-like on the very rim of her cranium, they might be brass washers, with glass beads, enamelled in the deepest blue, for pupils.

Not even the descent of night puts an end to their flat,

lidless stare. A twenty-five-cent piece could fit comfortably in one of the sockets.

Over the years, she had devoured many times her weight in fish, frogs, crayfish, and the like. Her wants were twice those of a male fish of equivalent size. And she grew faster than her male counterparts. But she is still far from her prime.

Her greed, as ever, knows no bounds. Because of her size, she has grown daily more ravenous. It takes more and more to fill her. Once she seizes a three-pound sucker broadside and bolts it in successive gulps. While it is yet mid way in her swallowing sac, stuffing her to the utmost, a fat perch sails into view. Her eyes say, Be after it! But annoyingly, the still flapping tail of the sucker gets in her way. And the startled perch is merely tumbled over and over in her head-long rush.

So skilled in attack has she become, the whole procedure is one of mechanical perfection. She can resist temptation for hours on end if need be, with hardly a quiver of fin to signal her presence. When the right moment comes, distance and placing of her leap are automatically calculated. With one violent thrust, fins and tail propel her to her mark, the subsequent upheaval of water and sound of jaws closing seeming to happen at one instant of time.

Her need to keep out of sight of her prey has put a fine edge on her cunning. And so she puts to greater and greater use the friendly shadows of the evening, the camouflage of rock and tree limb, the concealing canopies of floating vegetation.

There is more of her to hide now. So must she take greater pains in the process. When she resorts to a strategy of waiting (as she most often does) she likes to choose an old tree top where her markings will simulate the shadows of the dead branches. Due to this habit, her cross-bars have broken up into blotches. But when the protective cover is less diffuse, such as a single tree limb or a rock cleft, her skin pigmentation responds by reverting briefly to the barred pattern.

Always, she must lie so that she has a clear view of the

water lanes. Thus it is that, at times, sight of one malevolent yellow orb gives warning and she is cheated of her intended meal.

In spring and fall when fierce winds wrack the lake she feels upset and seeks out the deepest holes she can find, there awaiting the end of the turbulence. Following such periods, she cannot content herself with playing the waiting assassin. Instead, she ranges far and wide, feeding ravenously on whatever she comes across until her hunger is appeased.

At times—particularly when there is a lack of wind to circulate the water, or after a series of dull days when there is no photosynthesis to cause the weeds to give off oxygen—she feels indisposed. Low pressure periods, which adversely affect her metabolic processes, also see her inactive and with her appetite dulled.

Fishermen can seek her where they will when the wind is in the east: except on the rarest of occasions, she will be blind to their offerings. But let the wind change to the west, and she becomes her natural self once again. Then her predacious instincts reach their pinnacle.

Treachery has a place in her make-up, as who could doubt on viewing that cruel snout, low flat forehead and evil eye. She is a pirate, capable of any deceit to gain her ends. She would swallow her own brother, had she one. And indeed has many times—by purpose rather than accident—swallowed her own kind.

This happens when she is especially hungry. Then she prowls the dim corridors beside the weed forests. It is a dangerous place, for there, like gaunt tigers in their lairs, lie other muskellunge, awaiting passing prey. Her slightly luminous form, seldom fully seen, invites immediate attack. But she is ready. A sudden churning, a blurred shape, and she whirls to seize the enemy. Usually her greater speed and size enable her to emerge quickly victorious. But once she was not so lucky.

Other large muskellunge inhabit the lake. One of the largest is Cheeka, a splendid fish, a year or two older than

Ma-Kee. She has never bothered her rival for the simple reason that she respected the other's size. Nor had Ma-Kee molested Cheeka. But not for the same reason. It was that she had never had the chance.

The slowly sinking sun has dipped itself in the waters of the lake and left its colours like oil upon the surface. The bur reeds stand tall and unwavering amid the calm. Suddenly, at their outer edge, in the very heart of the golden saffron glow, a wild commotion occurs.

A large, strong fish, observing the wake of a water rat, has followed the animal into shallow water and seized it. Still with it crosswise in her jaws, the fish swims back to deep water.

At this juncture, attracted by the noise, Ma-Kee arrives on the scene. Recognizing Cheeka and deciding that she has her rival at a disadvantage, she launches herself at Cheeka's belly. But as she does so Cheeka wheels, instinctively opening her jaws and releasing her recently captured meal.

Straight into Ma-Kee's yawning mouth the unexpected morsel drops. But now she, in turn, is at a disadvantage. Before she can gulp it down, Cheeka, infuriated, has seized her in front of her tail. It is a clean bite, taking away part of a fin together with a piece of flesh fortunately no larger than Ma-Kee can afford to lose.

The water in the area is now coloured a deeper red than any left by the sun's rays, and Ma-Kee thinks better of her original purpose. Swiftly she retreats, lucky that Cheeka, with the taste of blood, does not follow her.

In due course the wound heals. A furrow is left, completely covered over with scar tissue. Even the torn anal fin regenerates. But the mark remains in evidence.

These are but a few of the scars Ma-Kee bears. Fortunately, she profits by her lessons. She knows by now that if she is to eat and not be eaten, she can ill afford to be rash.

Man, the predator she had most reason to fear, has wrought her little harm. Several times since the episode with Old Ame she has been beguiled into taking a fisherman's bait, but she has managed each time to break free. On one occasion, indeed, the fisherman's life was in greater jeopardy than hers.

Alone in the boat, he was alternately casting and retrieving a perch, from which he had removed the back fin, when, with an audacity he could not quite believe, a huge muskellunge swam to within a yard of the boat, seized the perch and swam off with it.

In the moment that followed, the angler so let his astonishment overcome him that he failed to give line. The line was weak because he had lazily left it wet on the spool too many times. And so, it parted.

The angler, however, not to be so easily robbed of his prize, threw caution to the winds and jumped overboard, clutching blindly at the trailing line. He barely missed. It was enough, though, to lose him his chance. For Ma-Kee, hearing the thunderous noise, put on speed and was soon far from the scene.

Now the fisherman was in a plight. His boat had drifted away and he must make for the shore. He was only a fair swimmer and the weight of his clothes made progress difficult. More by luck than skill, he dragged himself ashore half drowned.

"The idea!" his wife said that night. "You must have taken leave of your senses."

But the angler didn't think so. And afterward grinned to himself when he thought about it. What was life without a little excitement? Besides, the fish was a trophy fish if he ever saw one.

Within minutes of her taking it, the perch reposed, hook and all, in Ma-Kee's stomach. The line gave her a bit of trouble but, in due course, it followed the perch. The hook was one of several that had lodged in her gut. Old Ame's hook, caught in her jaw, had long since rusted and broken away.

Waxing constantly greater, Ma-Kee's diet had widened. Forage fish such as dace and perch she gobbled up almost faster than the eye could see. But these and suckers (a favourite food) were not always as plentiful as she would like. She took to supplementing her bill of fare with all sorts of substitutes.

On one occasion, in a marshy inlet where winged life abounded, on impulse she suddenly broke water and caught a low-flying swallow as neatly as a trout takes a fly. The experience was more than worth while, for it taught her that a feathered morsel was equally as desirable as one with scales. The swallow made quite a comfortable lump in her stomach. True, it took longer to digest. But in many ways that fact had its advantages.

In June, when mother ducks took to the water with their broods, the more observant among them glimpsed Ma-Kee's ominous shadow in time and, fluttering frantically, managed to shepherd at least part of their families to the safety of the reeds. Those that didn't and whose flocks were convoyed by the gaunt fish, wound up the day with many less than had started out; often with none at all.

At a discreet distance, Ma-Kee picked off the stragglers. If she was discovered, she discarded all pretence and bent her efforts to gobbling as many of the fuzzy tidbits as she could take into her jaws at one time before beating a retreat.

At such times the marsh resounded with the alarmed quacks of the beleaguered flotillas, and other creatures within hearing remained still. In the presence of Terror it is well to know whom it is stalking.

Fur, Ma-Kee also found, was not at odds with her digestive capacities. And so the water rats and mice and such like of the locality found themselves with an enemy they had perhaps not counted on.

And now comes a day when this extension of her feeding habits very nearly costs Ma-Kee her life. The time is early spring, just after the ice break-up. In the marsh, a few thin snow-coated slabs still drift about, occasionally bumping with a creaking sound into the glassy ice-layer where the rushes stand locked. By mid morning, as has been the pattern for a week or more, the rushes will be free of their night-born yoke.

Already the voice of the red-winged blackbird is upon the land. But not yet has that other herald of spring in the marsh country, the thunder-pumper, arrived on the scene.

Old Ame is abroad, for once with legitimate purpose. He has a licence to take muskrats in the area and for several days now has had his traps set. Each morning he starts out to collect his catch, carefully resetting those of his traps that have been sprung, relocating others that have failed to produce.

He is wearing hip-waders, for there is much sloshing through icy water to be done on the job. And when going from one trap to another, wool-lined leather mitts help take the sting out of his hands.

Ordinarily he does not burden himself with unnecessary equipment. But today, in addition to the worn canvas haversack strapped about his shoulders, he carries a shotgun. It is loaded and ready, and as he goes about his work his watery blue eyes sweep expectantly over the rough, rush-fringed terrain. Now and again he pauses, leaning forward to brush the ground with his fingers, as though examining it for tracks. This action he accompanies with sidelong glances in the direction of the nearby bush, or by taking a step or two off course so that he can more readily scrutinize areas of special interest.

From one inlet to another he moves, his body, leviathan-like, shutting out whole patches of distant woods, shoulders thrust rudely into the keen blue of the sky. His head, togged in leather helmet, even eclipses the sun.

The air is brisk and sweet-smelling. The breeze that bends the dry ribbons of swamp grass stirs also the life within.

The first two traps give up rats. The third, which he has to reach through knee-deep water, is not at first in evidence. The log to which it had been fastened is still there, though, and so must the trap be unless it has been stolen.

Probing under it with a stick, he locates the chain. In a

moment he drags the trap into view. It is sprung, but grimly clutches only the head and front quarters of the muskrat. A hollow victory for both trap and man.

Old Ame cannot resist an exclamation of anger. It has happened again!

And now, the reason for the shotgun is evident. Something —bird, animal, or water dweller—has been stealing his catch. Twice before he has lost rats in the same fashion, torn forcibly from the trap. Once, only a paw remained.

He suspected foxes. Only a large strong creature could accomplish the feat, and the marks of powerful canine teeth suggested some such animal. But each of the robberies had taken place where the water was deepest and where, as a rule, there was only the most difficult access to the trap from the shore. He had seen foxes jump logs: there was no trick to that. But not across several feet of water. A snapping turtle perhaps, he ruminates. Well, let the marauder, whatever it was, beware. There is much of cunning in the old poacher, too. And with the loss of skins to sharpen his zeal, he will be a relentless pursuer.

On the way to the next trap he proceeds cautiously, holding his gun at ready. His path is along a narrow spit of land. Halfway, a natural cleavage in the rushes occurs and here, where the water swings to meet the shore, he has arranged his set. A stout sapling, felled and wedged between two stakes, provides anchorage for the trap.

Approaching the spot, he is not prepared for what he sees, and so is slow in bringing his gun into action. The sapling has been imbued with motion. It is being tugged vigorously by some invisible agency, causing the far end alternately to submerge and rise to the surface, each time with a hollow chug, and to send hosts of feverish wrinkles chasing one another in confusion outward from the disturbed area.

The accomplishment is far beyond a muskrat's power were it alive in the trap and struggling to be free. What, then, can it be?

The old poacher's eyes, quickly locating the spot from

which the tugging was being done—slightly past and to one side of the sapling's tip—strained for some identification of the cause. The notion strikes him instantly that he is witnessing the theft of one of his rats. Simultaneous with this conclusion what he sees causes him to draw in a quick breath.

A cessation of the splashing quiets the water, allowing him to make out the lines of a large, powerfully built fish. The head at first looks to be that of a lizard or enormous turtle, for only Ma-Kee's leathery snout is clearly to be seen. She has hold of the muskrat's furry body and, with jaws clenched, looks reptilian indeed.

Old Ame needs no second glance to go into action. Swiftly raising the gun, he fires, the charge making a pock-marked crater over the spot where the fish had been. But, with the smoothing of the surface, the marauder was nowhere in evidence.

Fast as Old Ame had been, Ma-Kee was faster, withdrawing the instant the gleam of worn gun barrel in the sunlight had flashed her warning. She has escaped the full force of the charge. As it is, she is momentarily stunned, but not enough to prevent her swimming weakly to deeper water. A second shot, fired on chance, merely spurs her to greater effort.

Several of the lead pellets have entered her side. It is an unfamiliar hurt, bringing with it a series of stinging pains.

As for the old poacher, a few scales churned up in the ferment of Ma-Kee's retreat give him the satisfaction of knowing he has scored at least a partial hit.

He knows enough not to tell the story of the large fish. Few would believe him. Besides, it is a long time since he has seen a muskellunge so big. He will wait his opportunity and go after it with rod and line.

Later that spring there is a revival of the muskellunge study by the biologists. A new group back in the city has acquired funds for a fresh start. Already a site has been selected: a river, flowing to the lake, on which, some years before, a temporary dam had been erected. By reinforcing the dam and thereby raising the water level, they have at their disposal a marshy lake, some acres in extent, which, together with the flooded river, should make ideal muskie cover.

But first they must have stock. Later, the hatchery will supply them with fry and fingerlings. However, as the project area is plentifully supplied with food, they are anxious to introduce adult fish as well.

To do this, they have set a trap net, planning to work it for several weeks. The muskellunge will continue to move until the hot weather comes. By then, they should have caught and transported quite a fair number of fish.

The net is a ponderous affair. Ashore, before setting, it had lain a seemingly hopeless jumble of rope and mesh, lead weights hanging like satiated bloodsuckers amid its sprawling folds, with every so often the bulging shape of a cylindrical metal float. But, in the water, with what diabolical cunning it has been vested!

It has taken two men almost a full morning to set. Several feet from shore is the trap—a large, mesh-enclosed chamber, completely submerged, which is the final converging point for fish lured to the net. Far out in deep water is the lead. This is a six-foot-deep barrier of net, designed to impede the fish and precipitate the chain reaction which, by various stages, will lead it to the trap. Between the lead and trap are the wings: two lengths of net which radiate from the lead to further direct the progress of the potential captive. Then, successively, the house and funnel.

By turning back in a direct line, once having entered the house, a fish could readily escape. To either side, it would encounter the hearts, twin cul-de-sacs attached to the wings which, in due course, narrow to nothingness. About face, then, at either of these junctures, and onward through the house.

Escape is still a possibility. But now, with stealthy ingenuity, the net narrows into a funnel which, at its terminal point, is hardly more than eight inches in diameter. Through this, and all is lost. For beyond lies the trap.

Cunning indeed. The hundred-foot lead is even tarred, the more effectively to turn the victim. And hearts and house have been treated with cuprinol to give them the greeny cast of the weeds.

Ma-Kee, one day, chancing on the lead, follows it unwittingly to the house. Once inside, her curiosity urges her forward. Other fish are in the net too. The farther she goes, the more congested it becomes until, finally, she is one of a seething mass. She turns back. But the way she came seems to have vanished.

She is trapped.

The Bay of Herons

T H E net was not lifted until the following afternoon. By that time, Ma-Kee had recovered somewhat from the alarm she first felt on discovering she was imprisoned.

Bass, pickerel, muskellunge, perch, suckers, throngs of sunfish, nosed about in the gloom. The mesh prison even quartered its share of bullheads, which restlessly worked their way back and forth over the floor of the net, creating a regular stir of mud. Only the fact that the trap was six feet in all directions made it possible to breathe freely.

Most of the time, Ma-Kee spent in the upper confines of the net where the water was clearer. When she tired of this she sank to the bottom, taking up position close to one of the side walls. This was not nearly so satisfactory for breathing. And she must suffer the indignity of being shoved and buffeted and even used as a resting place. But it permitted her to conserve her energy. The opportunity to escape might come at any moment. She must be ready.

Finally a boat with two men draws alongside the net. The roof of the trap has a large opening, laced with twine. When unlaced, the opening will give the men access to the booty within. But first the trap must be drawn to the surface.

After quite a bit of tugging and pulling, dark folds of netting crowd the side of the boat, the vent is unlaced and the fish exposed.

One by one, the larger fish are removed. All muskellunge and some of the bass (the latter to help provide a balanced population) are transferred quickly to a retainer net which has been staked in a handy position nearby. The rest of the fish are scooped or thrown back in twos and threes as they come into view. It is quite impossible to rid the net entirely of the unwanted varieties, they are in such numbers. Later, the net can be turned on its side and those that are left be permitted to escape at random. Until the men are sure no muskellunge have gone undetected, however, the probing and peering must continue.

How right they are to take such precautions!

Large as she is, Ma-Kee has so far remained hidden from view. Down in one corner of the net she waits her chance. She has no explanation for the fearful goings-on above her. Two circumstances only impress themselves on her shallow brain : that the gash of light in which all the disturbance has taken place is, for brief intervals now, quite free of activity; and that the crush of fish has lessened.

By selecting the right moment, she may gain a clear path to safety. She almost succeeds.

During a lull, in which the men rest with the butts of their hands on the boat's gunwale, she comes charging upward. The sudden upheaval from the net's murky depths and the sight of Ma-Kee's great head cause them to rear back, startled. But, in doing so, they shift the net, which they still clutch, unintentionally deflecting her leap so that she loses momentum and falls sideways. The thwarted leap carries her, instead of to safety, almost into their grasp.

She is slippery and a weight to test their strength, so awkward is the business of securing her. But two pairs of hands soon manage and she is safely deposited with her fellows. A big spawner! Luck is surely with them.

In due course the captives are transferred to metal tanks, which are placed on a truck for the journey to the sanctuary. Ma-Kee requires a tank all to herself. Even so, she feels suffocated, and is only partly relieved by the jouncing of the truck as it travels the rough dirt roads.

The last stage of the journey is through a regular tunnel

of foliage of all kinds. Low-growing plants and flowers, bushes, and trees of sapling size, rise in green confusion on either side of the road. The very heavens seem clothed in verdure, for the taller vegetation leans to shut out the sky. Raspberry cane forms a prickly bulwark for every growing thing that is shoulder-high or less. Its protective ranks seem almost to guarantee the safe blossoming, a month later, of the pearly everlasting and gentian that rub shoulders with the long-since flowering bloodroot.

Now, as though into a shimmering sea, the sudden plunge into daylight once more. Ahead is the river, sprawling heart of the flooded jungle through which it flows. And, to one side, the collection of worn grey buildings that once formed the office, bunkhouse, and storage sheds of the lumber mill that operated there in years gone by. A trifle ramshackle, perhaps; but with mended roofs and suitable furnishings they do very nicely as the project's headquarters. Here, in some modicum of comfort, the biologists can be on the job throughout the summer.

At last Ma-Kee's journey is ended. At the river's edge, she is eased into the water with the others. It is an auspicious occasion. The project is under way.

From the point at which Ma-Kee has been deposited, it is perhaps a mile to the man-made lake and several miles to the sanctuary's upper limits. The flooding, years before, has bloated the river. But its additional width is at the expense of what was originally the shoreline. The separation is still distinct, marked by a wild profusion of surface vegetation that follows the river's tenuous path as evenly as the grass along a garden sidewalk.

Now narrowing, now widening, as dictated by the contours of the higher land beyond, the flooded areas have become still, pool-pocketed morasses. They have become, as well, ghostly graveyards for trees that, long before, surrendered to the liquid death. Stiff, bark-bare, dismembered, shattered, they stand singly and in colonies, presenting a woeful memory of what once had been.

Willow-sprouting stumps tell how, for a time, the water receded. Its new level has once more taken them to its watery bosom and claimed also new hosts of growing things. Clinging now to their temporary lease on life, they too will soon smother and decay.

This, then, is Ma-Kee's new home: a dead world above, over much of its extent, but a riotous, thronging living world below.

A majestic silence hangs over all. It is an area of desolation; of little-travelled roads; of bristling, unending bushland; of wide and empty sky; of slow-flowing water artery. The fish hawk, a poised speck in the heavens, owns it. The frog, hunched on his lily pad by the rushes, owns it. The dragonfly, stiff darting on fairy wings, owns it. So too do the leaf beetles, inexorable conquerors of the oval-leaf potamogetons, and the army of bugs and fishes and sundry other creatures that inhabit the waters of river and lake.

Now, even more truly, Ma-Kee, in turn, takes it unto herself.

It is inevitable that Ma-Kee soon finds her way to the lake. Opposite the dam, an arm broadens into a narrow bay. Here, in a branch of the riverbed, where the water is deepest, she elects to make her stand.

There is plenty of food; a wondrous entanglement of trees, stumps, algae, and water plants to give her hiding. And she has but to round the bend to be back in the main course of the river.

The bay is also the nesting place of a colony of blue herons. The great birds roost in the lofty branches of a willow forest overlooking the bay. They come from great distances at night, settling in to the accompaniment of harsh barking, their grotesque bodies hovering and turning, wings beating ever faster as they approach the tree tops, legs dropping at the last moment like the landing gear of airplanes.

Largest of their family, they require such well-watered, out-of-the-way places for the perpetuation of the species. They feed in the marshy areas of the surrounding lakes; and in the sanctuary, too. No predator—man, bird or beast—is a more patient fisher. Krark, the heron, depends on this quality of unwavering restraint as much as on his pile-driver beak. He knows how to use both to advantage.

His beak is a murderous weapon. Powered by his long, curving neck, it can split the shell of a snapping turtle. So true is its aim, so delicate its perception, a minnow is snared as easily as a much larger fish.

The mysteries of light refraction puzzle Krark not at all. Since he could first wade spindle-legged after his mother, he has learned to overcome a whole series of such problems. He had to. Upon his skill depends his very life.

The herons are quite at home in the bay. The shallow cluttered reaches afford them good wading—and, with the plenitude of finned inhabitants, good fishing. And the profusion of tree skeletons, echoing their own grey-blue colour and gnarled shape, makes a perfect background for their activities.

In the early morning as daylight, like absorbent paper, blots up the dark vestiges of night, they rise one by one from their tree roosts and fly off to the wet places. When they have done feeding, they often stay where the last morsel had been obtained, cleaning themselves or settling on one leg to rest and digest the contents of their craws.

On such a morning, as the herons stand hunched like harpies at intervals in the shore waters, Ma-Kee enters the scene.

She is abnormally hungry today. A strong north wind has kept her confined to her hole for almost forty-eight hours— much too long for her liking. She craves something large; so large that it will quell the torment in her stomach.

Krark, nearby, is standing knee-deep in water, contentedly absorbing the first warm rays of the sun.

The legs of the heron first come into view. Staring upward through her window, Ma-Kee makes out Krark's bloated form. Rash though her decision is, the nearness of so gargantuan a meal is too much for her.

Boldly she seizes Krark's leg and with all her strength proceeds to drag him into deep water.

It is a fantastic sight—had anyone been there to see. Roused so horribly from his lethargy, it is moments before Krark comprehends what is happening. Yet his reactions are instinctive and save him instant drowning.

Ma-Kee has reckoned without the great wings which, even as Krark is pulled sleepily off balance, commence to beat frantically and, while his upswung head voices hoarse alarm, manage to pull her half out of the water. Krark's beak now goes into action. Twice he gets in stabbing, vicious thrusts before Ma-Kee's weight drags him down again.

Red pours from Ma-Kee's wounds but she hangs on grimly.

Now Krark's breast touches the water, and finally, his wings, flopping soggily in and out like a boy flogging at water bugs with a willow branch. His feathers keep him afloat but he was long ago doomed.

Weakly he strikes at his now unseen adversary, his head reared like a serpent's. A crow, wounded, in the retriever's jaws, will strike at his captor thus.

Great circles radiate out from the place where Krark disappears. And for brief moments, the water rises in spasms from below.

It is most of a day before Ma-Kee realizes she has bitten off more than she can chew. Wide as she can force her jaws, Krark's body is wider. Finally, by taking the now limp neck halfway and gulping it double, she gets Krark down to where the breast begins. With that she has to be content. She can consume no more of him. But her digestive organs will accomplish the dissolution of neck from body.

She is in no hurry. Besides, her wounds call for a period of convalescence.

A last lucky thrust by Krark has partly dislodged one of her eyes.

Never had Ma-Kee fed so well as she did in the sanctuary. Food abounded, with few predators to give her competition.

Even in the winter it was not necessary to travel far when she felt hungry. For practically the whole fish population was forced to congregate in the deep holes to avoid being frozen with the ice. She simply took food as she needed it.

From time to time she was caught in nets set to determine the progress of the planted fish. Each time, one of her fins was clipped and details noted of corresponding size and weight.

In the spring her fierce heart warmed enough to allow her to spawn and thus fulfil the hopes of the biologists. When she had done, she seized her companion of the courtship and swallowed him head first. Then she resumed her eternal quest for food.

But alas. Her paradise was too good to last. After two years the project operators, finding that their small-mesh nets turn up few medium-sized muskies, attribute the fact to cannibalism and reluctantly return her, with other large she-fish, to the lake.

But before doing so, they put a tag on her. A small rectangle of plastic bearing a number and the project name, attached to her opercle by means of a fine wire.

At least they will have a record of her if she is caught.

The blaze of afternoon descends on the still waters of the inlet as on a myriad scattered sequins. It is a quiet place, suited to repose. But for the tiny winking fires and peripatetic flights of winged insects, the whole area seems at rest. Occasionally a backswimmer, stroking upward with oar-like legs, pierces the water surface. But its emergence is so brief the disruption goes almost unnoticed.

Now comes another disturbance. The wild celery is in bloom and, from the base of the graceful blades, male flowers begin to leave their anchorage. Upward they soar, one by one, here and there over the fields of streaming weed, each clasping the tiny balloon of air that is its means of ascendance. Softly they emerge, and slowly unfold their petals in response to the sun's down-pouring rays.

It is a glorious thing to exist—bird, fish or insect, weed or organism—here in this inlet. Compressed into a unit, the great heart and pulse of it all must stir the world to its very foundations.

Soon, a male flower—propelled by the slight movements of the summer air, drifts to where the female flowers, like embryonic parasols, are held aloft on spiralling tendrils. No chance meeting, this. For others, in due course, join the first. Now the sticky pollen of the drifting blooms adheres to the female flowers and, in the brief union, a new cycle of life begins.

Not a moment too soon. For, of a sudden, the gentle scene explodes with a violence that bends the water plants as through the agency of some furious subterranean wind. Waves flee the spot, bearing the floral flotsam on their serpent backs. Then, swiftly, fearsomely, all is as before, but now the knowledge of peril is within the boundaries of the inlet.

A bass, cruising unconcernedly, had not reckoned the telltale lines of the grim monster that for an hour lay camouflaged in a nearby bed of elodea. For his carelessness he is seized in one mighty leap.

Ma-Kee, mistress of the lake, is back. Her return marks an end to tranquillity.

On the Ice

ALTHOUGH Moses Todd had long suspected Old Ame of owning a gill net, he had never caught the old poacher with one in his possession. The reason was, Ame confined his gill netting to the wintertime.

Setting a net under the ice was a feat beyond the ken of all save Old Ame. Few would have thought it possible or even worth while. Certainly the Warden, as well as any others who might have been interested, gave no thought to such a probability. And so Old Ame was able to carry on his activities in this particular direction with little fear of discovery.

The feat was difficult. But with his poacher's cunning, Ame had mastered it.

His method, learned on the prairies in his younger days, was to use a jigger. This consisted of a cedar plank about six feet long, slotted to receive a wooden lever. When he wished to set the net, he first cut a hole in the ice and thrust the jigger under. The plank, floating hard against the ceiling of ice, was then propelled forward by working a rope attached to the wooden lever. As it went, it trailed a line which unwound from a coil on the ice.

It was a simple affair for one person to operate. The noise the jigger made told him how far it was from the hole, and its exact location. By chopping another hole at that point, he was able to remove the jigger and the attached line. With the line, he then strung the length of net under the ice between the two holes.

There was no denying the ingeniousness of the device, nor

Ame's enjoyment in its use. On many a winter day he had chuckled to himself as he hauled in his catch : bass, muskellunge and, latterly, pickerel aplenty. The pickerel fell easy prey to the net, their sharp sloping heads fitting neatly into the diamond-shaped mesh, armoured gill covers effectively preventing them from withdrawing.

Ame's enjoyment on such occasions, though voiced lightly, was caught up and echoed by the winds. What wouldn't Moses Todd give to see him then !

It was with such an inward chuckle that Old Ame journeyed forth one day in February to lift the net he had set two days before. Slower now than in years gone by, he plodded in a straight line across the frozen surfaces of bay and inlet, continuing on an almost straight course through intervening brush patches, to the spot.

Hidden among the trees, conveniently near, was the sleigh on which he had borne net and jigger. There was a basket, too, for the fish, and an ice chisel fashioned out of a crowbar. He had travelled by night to get the equipment to the scene. He would travel by night on his return.

The previous forty-eight hours had been bitter cold. This, he knew, meant rechopping the holes. But one hole, at least, did not need to be large. As the net would be drawn out at one point, the other hole had to be opened only enough to loosen the ropes that secured it.

There was some consolation in that : for chopping was no easy task.

As he began, he thought with satisfaction that it would not be overly long before his catch was in the basket and he could start back. He had left two hours for the job before dusk set in. The thought of the glowing red belly of his Quebec heater, his chair and pipe, warmed him against the keen wind. More than ever nowadays, he sought their comfort. He was old now, quite old, and he knew it. Well, he would not have to venture forth again with his net this winter. Frozen, his catch should last him well into spring.

Soon he has the larger hole newly opened and moves on to

the next. He is a bit tired and his veined hands shake as he lights his pipe preparatory to renewing his attack on the flint-hard ice. Far out on the lake where the wind is a strong broom, the ice has the black look of ebony. From time to time he can hear hollow noises like distant gunshots as the great fields react to the alternate tortures of expansion and contraction. But here in the shelter of the shoreline the snow has held, forming a sponge-textured crust little different in appearance from that of the land around.

This crust was already scraped and kicked away over an area somewhat wider than the hole, thus easing his task. Now the chisel bites in and, little by little, he gains access to the rough, slanting opening he had made two days before. At last the chisel breaks through, but with a suddenness that takes it out of his hands. Fortunate that the old man's thoroughness extended to a rope loop tied through an eye in the chisel handle. This, around his arm, abruptly halts the chisel's downward journey, which would have seen the precious instrument lost to sight under the ice.

With the break-through quickly enlarged to a comfortable opening, Ame starts to free the ropes. They have been tied to a stake set back a piece from the hole. The knots are frozen and hard to untie. Ropes and netting, too, must be released from their icy entombment at the edge of the hole.

When this is done, a further difficulty faces him. In some inexplicable manner the net has got caught below the surface —possibly on the limb of a submerged tree, or on a ragged projection of ice. Until he frees it, the net cannot be recovered through the far hole.

This is a turn of events he has not reckoned on. Darkness is not far off. He must hurry.

On his knees, he prods at the ice with the ice chopper. But this is awkward at best. The only simple alternative, straining on the ropes in an attempt to tear the net free, might result in serious damage.

At last he knows what he must do. Removing his heavy outer coat, he rolls up one shirt sleeve and, lying full length on the ice, reaches down through the narrow opening. He can sense where the net is caught. But he cannot quite reach the point.

Well below the ice ceiling, his hand strains and gropes blindly, fingers stretched to the utmost in a desperate attempt to find the obstacle. The water is cruelly numbing. Another instant and he will have to acknowledge defeat.

He has partly withdrawn his arm when, with mingled pain and shock, he feels his hand seized as though by a dog, with a dog's strong jaws and a dog's sharp teeth, and a jolting force jerks him downward to his armpit.

The unexpectedness of the happening, the wild imaginings and pain that accompany it, bewilder him; leave him flat-stretched and open-mouthed, conscious of the comforting solidity of the ice and the protective barrier it formed between him and this strange thing that was happening below.

His mysterious attacker was large and strong. Of that there was no doubt. His hand was its captive. And it was busy now, fangs deeply imbedded, threshing and twisting in an attempt to drag the captive away.

Almost as quickly as it had begun, the event was over. For Old Ame had had many scrapes with danger in his lifetime, even if nothing as unusual as this, and his matter-of-fact nature quickly came to his rescue.

Rearing up, a harsh ejaculation on his lips, he lifts his arm with all his strength. In the narrowness of the hole he can just catch sight of the creature that has attacked him before it lets go.

A huge muskie! Probably feeding off his net. Not strange that it had attacked him, for his hand and arm would be no larger than any fat pickerel still alive and threshing in the mesh.

Upright, the old man squeezes a large coloured handkerchief about his hand to stem the bleeding. He is unsteady on his feet and shaking with the cold. The incident has caused all thoughts of net and fish to evaporate. Foremost in his mind is that he must get on his coat. He will feel better then.

The hole is now between him and the coat. But he is only remotely conscious of the fact. His first faltering step forward brings his foot directly above the narrow opening before he realizes the danger. Too late, he sidesteps. His heavy boot meets the slippery ice slope, throwing him off balance. His full weight is on the imperilled leg and with a sucking sound his foot goes deep into the hole.

In the plunge, his shin is badly bruised and it is moments before he can bring himself to attempt an escape from his new plight.

Cautiously at first, on one knee, he raises the trapped leg. So tight is the fit in the choked enclosure it comes no farther than his boot top. Again he tries, bending more energy to the effort. But though he succeeds in freeing the boot top, his most desperate struggles will not loosen the grip of the encircling ice.

A vain attempt now, to undo the lace of the imprisoned boot. But even as his fingers pry at the leather strands, already ice-glazed, he realizes the effort is futile. The boot is so deep in the hole that only the top criss-crossings of lace are exposed. Not even cutting them with his pocket knife would loosen the top sufficiently to enable him to pull his foot free.

There is no way out, obviously, in that direction. Neither, with the same ineffectual blade, could he ever hope to conquer the twenty-inch thickness of ice.

The alarm he had felt in his encounter with Ma-Kee was as nothing compared with the raw fear that floods through him now.

The ice chisel!

It lies just beyond his coat, which is now within reach.

Stretching himself to his full length, he is still far short. Tears caused by the stinging wind mingle with his sweat, adding, in due course, to the glassy crystals that have gathered over the whole of his bristled face, like hoarfrost. In the west, beyond the pale glow of the wintry landscape, the sky is a dark veil.

Is he to be beaten by the elements he had bested for so long?

Restraining the panic that fights for supremacy, he resolutely surveys the situation. Failure to reach the ice chisel brings another thought.

Holding tight to a sleeve of the discarded coat, he flings the coat in the direction of the chisel. Hope becomes a frantic pain within him. The far sleeve has fallen across the iron bar. He had dared conceive that the coat's weight might move it and that successive casts would bring it nearer. Perhaps the cuff button will catch!

Momentarily stifling his now laboured breathing, he pulls ever so gently on the coat. But his hopes are dashed as the sleeve slides off ineffectually.

Again.... Again.... He must keep trying.

A second cast is no more successful. On the third, all the energy of his trembling frame is summoned for the purpose. But his damaged hand loses its hold, allowing the coat to continue in full flight to a point beyond his target.

Sitting back now, all avenues of escape having failed him, a fearsome calm settles over Old Ame. For some reason he has ceased to tremble. The loss of his coat, even, does not give him concern.

Idly, he wonders at this. His hands, he senses, are frozen—partly the result of attempting to undo the lace of his submerged boot. Perhaps the rest of him is slowly freezing.

Yes, that is it.

The tears that slowly well and trickle from beneath his frosted lids are not now the doing of the wind. Through eyes that hardly see, he peers at the hole. It must be some time now since he had last attempted to free himself, for what had been water around his leg is now ice.

Well, he will try again presently.

Gradually, his barrel-like frame hunches. The sheltering darkness comes down upon him as though in embrace.

When they found him, he was still in the same sitting

position, "Like as if," one of the search party recounted, "he was waiting for a bite." As a mark of respect, they did not bother to raise the net, leaving it to be claimed by the lake in the spring break-up.

It was quite clear what had happened. But the marks on his hand were never satisfactorily explained.

They mourned him—each in his own way, depending on the extent to which the old man had entered their lives. Moses Todd felt saddest of all. He would miss the old poacher.

As for Ma-Kee, having been attracted to the hole that Old Ame had made, she stayed. Cheated of one meal, she soon found the Fates were not altogether unkind.

Those fish trapped alive in the net lasted her until her savage attacks pulled it to shreds.

The City Sportsman

URING a spell of inclement summer weather there arrived one day at the lake a short, stout, showy man, rather like a stage butler as to form, for he seemed all waistcoat, who put up at the most expensive lodge and promptly let it be known that he was there to catch a muskie—a big one.

He had brought the works, he told the proprietor, indicating two large tackle boxes and a formidable array of shiny metal rod cases with which, in addition to a suitcase, the handyman laboured ahead of him.

He grinned as he said this, and the proprietor, who had got his back up a bit at his guest's bustling entrance, found the grin sufficiently disarming to experience a complete relaxing of his feelings; indeed, to take a shine to the man. For he was really not a bad fellow, this angler from the city. He had with him, too, a small brown cocker spaniel which gazed up at him with lolling tongue and seemed ever eager to be at his heels. So he must have some redeeming qualities.

Over the next two days, while the weather remained at a standstill, the visitor's redeeming qualities were put to a severe test. To his fellow guests he revealed himself as a scientific angler. His approach to fishing, he explained, was the indirect rather than the direct; the subtle in place of the straightforward. When fish were not caught by fishermen, was it because the fish were smarter? Not at all. It was because the angler's approach was wrong.

He gave as an instance of the scientific approach an

acquaintance with the conditions that affect the feeding of fish: atmospheric pressure, solar and lunar gravitational influence, winds, and so on. "Why try to catch fish when they're not hungry?" he maintained. "Get 'em when they're on the feed."

It appeared, by his account, that he had been highly successful in "catching 'em on the feed." He had taken many trophy fish in many places. Trophy fish were his objective.

Despite the apparent single-handedness of his exploits, he took the precaution at the outset to inquire about the availability of a first-class guide and, sight unseen, hired Little Tom for the week. He did not mention that he had never before caught a muskie. Neither did he reveal that, for all his recounted peregrinations, most of his fishing knowledge had come from books. He therefore remained something of an enigma to his enforced listeners, who wished heartily that the time would arrive when he would be proved either the spinner of tall tales they thought him or the accomplished fisherman he claimed to be. Behind his back they began calling him "the Baron."

Daily at breakfast he announced barometer reading, temperature, and wind direction. Arrival of the daily paper found him with pad and pencil studying the weather map. By linking together similar pressure conditions across the country, he explained amid dubious looks, he was then able to forecast the movement of the low pressure area that was causing the trouble.

On the afternoon of the third day, his weather report was optimistic.

Ostensibly to Little Tom—on hand for orders—but as well, obviously, to all others within hearing, he announced: "Barometer's on the rise. The cold front that's whipped up this raw spell is due to disperse overnight. With luck, we'll have the wind in the west to southwest by morning—and good fishing!"

It was a dangerous forecast, judging by the eye. The previous forty-eight hours had been miserable. Squally, wet, below-average temperature. The sullen sky gave no sign of let-up.

The portly forecaster, in fact, was the only one who proceeded with preparations for a day's outing; hence, when the morning dawned garbed in beauty, he alone among the besieged company of fishermen was able to set forth at a desirably early hour to take advantage of it.

Little Tom was impressed. There had been the smell of better weather in the wind. But this! He wondered if, indeed, his employer had not so ordered it. True, there was an almost complete lack of cloud, which would deprive their artificial lures of much-needed camouflage. But a breeze made the water spirited. And, as predicted, it was out of the west.

Score one for the Baron!

It was score two that night, for they arrived back with as nice a mess of bass as had been brought into the lodge in many a year.

Pressed for details when he could be approached alone, Little Tom was a laconic but enlightening witness to the events of the day.

They had gone, it seemed, to a spot Little Tom knew well: a rock shoal that at one time or other during the morning hours could usually be counted on to produce bass. The day was not a muskie day. Bass would do very well as a substitute.

But some trick of fortune, perhaps the weather, had caused the smallmouths to absent themselves from their customary feeding grounds. Until almost noon the men had tried various spots over the length of the shoal. By then, even Little Tom's patience had worn thin.

It was the Baron who had delivered them from the dilemma. While Little Tom prepared lunch on a nearby island, the Baron had circled the area in the boat, taking the depths at intervals with a plumb. When he had located the deepest hole, some distance from the shoal, he tied a large bobber to the top end of the plumb line, leaving the bobber floating until they were ready to resume fishing.

The Baron's next procedure following lunch was to lower

a device designed to secure temperature readings at selected levels. When he noted a sharp drop-off from warm to cold, he checked the depth and advocated that they fish at that level. It was from that time on, whether by luck or the Baron's strategy would never be known, that they had started to catch fish.

The revelation raised the Baron's stock several points. It went still higher the next day when his boat duplicated the feat with a nice string of pickerel. When, the third day out, he and Little Tom managed the hat trick with a pair of keeper muskies, the lodge people were prepared to admit grudgingly they had been mistaken.

It was a bitter pill to have to swallow, for in his hour of triumph the Baron became even more voluble than before. Over and over, eyes alight, pudgy cheeks distended like inflated paper bags, he recounted the details of his successes.

It was nothing, though. All a matter of knowing how.

As for muskies—why, muskies were overrated. They put up a fair fight, but were a cinch to catch. He might not, he revealed, even bother trying for another one.

Secretly, however, the city sportsman had different ideas. Boating the muskies had stirred him profoundly. Their animal-like attack and steely strength were, together, the epitome of what he desired in a fish. It did not matter that both had been hooked by Little Tom. The next time *he* would be the fortunate one.

His stay at the lake was almost over. From now on it would be muskies in earnest.

Next morning as they headed up the lake—guide, angler and dog—the angler sorted out his artificial lures. It was another fine day, with the possibility of cloud, and from time to time he looked up to catch Little Tom's eye and to gesture, beaming, with a broad sweep of his arm, at lake and sky. The Ojibway, who had come to look for these expressions of admiration for the manifestations of the Great Spirit whose palace was the sun but whose hand was everywhere, answered in turn on each occasion with a broad smile and an obedient casting of his eyes toward the vista thus revealed. So had his ancestors worshipped. So this white man worshipped. It gave Little Tom a good feeling toward the Baron.

He had a good feeling toward him in other ways, too.

During the previous days of fishing the angler, remaining in character despite the sharp diminution of his audience, had talked a great deal. Little Tom had a great respect for a talker, and the taller the angler's tales grew, likewise grew the Ojibway's respect. It did not matter that they did not ring true. The telling, itself, was grand.

Now the roar of the outboard motor and the cheerful slap of waves against the prow outlawed conversation. Presently, though, it would be the angler's turn.

By early afternoon, alternately casting and trolling, they had netted only a few fish, all undersized. When the Baron, for the first time, complained of their luck, Little Tom shrugged.

"Big ones here." Then, with quick humour: "Fish smart. Mebbe dey shrink w'en dey take bait; grow big again after."

By "here" he meant the large weed bed that had held their attention for an hour past. It was a great, rearing forest of pondweed; a subterranean tangle of stalk and leaf that, from its centre, stretched perhaps a quarter-mile in all directions. It was detectable by the eye even at a distance because of its calming influence on the water surface, and because of the flower spikes, not yet in bloom, that everywhere protruded.

Much of the bed lay deep, permitting trolling. The lanes and open spots of the shallower sections invited the artistry of the caster.

Overhead the flaming palace of the Great Spirit shines weakly through the glutinous cloud layer. There is a sense of dampness in the air that tells of high humidity. The weeds near the boat stand fully revealed. Without shadow, they are without mystery.

Little Tom, seated at the stern, draws on his homemade

pipe, the bowl patiently hollowed from a knot, the stem of hazelwood with the pith removed. Beneath the peak of his tweed cap his face is hewn copper, his eyes placid, yet as piercing within their depths as those of *mechegegoona*, the fish hawk. The Baron, casting listlessly and in none too expert a manner, has been attracted for some moments by a cloud in serpent form, stretching from horizon to horizon, that is in the process of breaking up into a myriad small serpents, each, in shape, exactly like the host. But Little Tom's eyes, as though in manner born, follow each cast through plunk of lure to final retrieve.

Through the Baron's mind is idly coursing the notion of telling Little Tom the story of the dragon's teeth which, upon being sown over the earth, like seed, sprang up as an army, when a movement by the Ojibway draws his eyes from the celestial miracle.

Little Tom has half risen, peering intently out over the glazed water surface to a point slightly beyond where the Baron's lure last fell. With little to go on save the pale yellow of wide-spaced fins, he had sensed, from his sitting position, the presence of a large fish. And now his trained glance, adjusting itself more quickly to the poor visual conditions than that of his companion, makes out enough detail to give the vision recognizable form.

"No cast," he cautions the Baron, who had just reeled in. "Big muskie."

With the hand that had pushed a warning at the other's rod arm, he points covertly at the spot.

"Where? Where?" The Baron, painstakingly gazing, feels a prickling on his neck. "I don't see anything."

It is a fish such as Little Tom has not seen since he was a boy; a fit chieftain of its tribe, but he knows it to be a squaw. The really great *kinonge* are always she-fish.

"Oh, my Lord! I see it now!"

In addition to the prickling, the Baron feels the sweat starting out of him. The fish seems as long as the boat. He could not have brought himself to cast had he been ordered to. His delicately balanced casting rod felt as incongruous for the task as a fencing foil in the hands of a gladiator.

"What'll we do?" he asks hoarsely.

"We no disturb. Come get another day when sky right."

At that moment, in any event, Ma-Kee chose to depart. As easily as she had come, she turned and slipped away into the weeds, a great smoky hole showing where she disappeared.

She had a full stomach and was not interested in the pale awkward fish she had seen swimming back and forth in the vicinity of the boat. Often she followed boats curiously at a distance. Perhaps she nursed the hope that one day one of the young might fall off its parent's back. What a wonderful meal it would make!

Back at camp, the lodge people found themselves with a new version of the Baron on their hands—thoroughly chastened yet excited beyond control.

"It must have weighed fifty pounds," he estimated before his amused audience. And really, he was not far wrong. But they did not believe him.

He had seen, they concluded, a big carp, which species had recently invaded the lake, or a log. It was an excuse for having returned with a bare stringer.

So far as Little Tom was concerned, he had said nothing that would either confirm or deny the tale. Of course, he was not one to reveal the truth of such a matter lest his revelation lead another to the fish.

Acting thus on behalf of his employer, the absence of his testimony saw the latter hoist wrongfully on the petard of his own imagination.

The angler overstayed his time two days. Feverishly each day, with Little Tom at the motor, he trolled the area of the weed bed. Gone was the fine tackle. In its place he used a heavy trolling rod, fitted with the stoutest line the village tackle shops could provide. For lures he selected several large wooden plugs, each bristling with hooks.

But incessant effort failed to attract the monster fish.

The morning of the last day dawned to a sky very like a

mass of cotton wadding, dyed a dusky blue, that had been pushed and prodded up against the concave face of heaven; serene, sun-shielding.

A fisherman's sky! The angler almost shouted in excitement at sight of it. The big muskie must almost certainly be on the move this morning.

He was very nervous. He had not slept well since the incident. The guests at the lodge, he now realized, regarded him mockingly. Even his dog had sensed something was wrong and was quieter than usual in his company.

Over and over he conjured up pictures of hooking the big muskellunge; of the struggle of landing it; of his triumphant reception at the lodge; of the monster stuffed and reposing over his mantelpiece at home.

And now he was to have his last chance.

A wind had come up before they arrived at the weed bed, making the water choppy. Little Tom skirted the denser weeds, trolling on their fringe, for it was not possible to spy clusters in time to sidestep them with the lure. And a lure encumbered with weed was as ineffective as no lure at all.

They trolled at a good speed, which Little Tom deemed wise where muskies were concerned. Up, down, around, back.

It seemed an endless business before the strike. One moment the angler was seated staring resignedly out over his rod tip. The next he was on his knees struggling with a rod that threatened to be torn from his grasp. There were no words. Boat, men and fish suddenly were a single raw nerve amid a great emptiness.

Ma-Kee has taken the lure from above, coming down on it in a savage hawk-swoop. Its wig-wag motion, however, has caused her to aim short, delivering only the painted wooden body to her jaws. Into this her teeth have sunk a third of their length. The three treble hooks, like gleaming barbels, are miraculously appended just beyond.

Her back, exposed in the charge, looks for a moment like a sand spit after a receding wave. She feels no alarm, and so allows her momentum to carry her onward, coming to a stop deep in the weeds a few feet from the boat's stern.

Although they cannot see her, Indian and white man both sense what has happened. It is all the Baron can do to reel in the slack line, so fast has been the forward charge. When he sees it becoming taut again and realizes the nearness of the big muskellunge a shiver starts up in him. His hands and arms suddenly feel limp.

Using the gunwale for support, he rises to his feet. Little Tom, who had stopped the motor the instant of the strike, half kneels, half sits, brown fingers showing pale where they clutch the gaff handle. An air of puzzlement pinches his thick brows.

"Him in no hurry. You sure he still on?"

The slightest lift of the rod tip was all the Baron dared. His nervous nod affirmed direct connection of line with fish.

"Mebbe him not hooked—jus' hold plug," guessed Little Tom correctly.

The thought so alarmed the Baron that he forgot his nervousness.

"That's it!" he exclaimed excitedly. "I didn't have a chance to set the hooks. I'd better strike him."

Even had he been tempted to stop his employer, Little Tom would have been too late. For, with the words, the Baron struck heavily. Probably it wouldn't have mattered what course he took. The outcome, one way or another, was inevitable.

What happened then brought fish, men and dog into the fray.

Under the impetus of the strike, Ma-Kee came upward, departing the water like a log that has shot the rapids and reappears, standing on end for brief, teetering moments.

At the sight, the cocker spaniel, which had been lying quietly but attentively on the bow seat, springs into action.

Barking furiously, it quickly manoeuvres past gasoline tin, tackle boxes and other gear and thence, because it is the easiest path, through its master's legs, almost upsetting him.

Ma-Kee is down, with a great splash, still with the plug impaled on her teeth. But immediately she is away at a breakneck pace. And the Baron, off balance, is unable to give attention to the swiftly unwinding reel spool to prevent the line tangling.

A sudden moment of tension: of bending rod and taut line. Then the activating force is gone. With the slackening of the line, the angler voices his disappointment.

"Gone! He's gone!"

It is a wail. A piteous ejaculation of despair. Morosely he sinks into the seat, staring out at the scene of the catastrophe. In sight is only the plug, bobbing on the surface. Somehow the muskie had got free of it.

"Gone!" Now that it is over, he can hardly believe it happened; that he had actually struck the big fish and lost it. Never again in his lifetime would he have such a chance.

Inevitably, his thoughts turn to the lodge. He has hooked the big fish. But, as before, they will not believe him. He has no proof.

No proof? His eyes widen, staring at the wooden lure, which he has idly reeled in. But merely staring is not sufficient confirmation. He reaches out, taking the plug gingerly in his fingers, examining it, unbelievingly at first, then delightedly, even rapturously.

His chuckle erases all trace of his former mood.

It is true! And he passes the wooden plug to Little Tom to show him the three teeth, the largest fully an inch long judging from what is to be seen of it, protruding from the back. Plainly broken off in the encounter. Here is evidence with a vengeance!

Back at the lodge the story was told; the plug displayed.

The Baron left, exalted in the eyes of all. What had seemed the tallest of his tall tales had been corroborated completely. But he left with a conviction that adventures of this kind were perhaps a mite nerve-wracking for a man of his years.

It was not likely that the north country would see him again.

The Intruders

GARG, the big bull carp, is on the rampage. It is June, spawning time of the carp, and Garg has been robbed of his intended mate. Several male carp, fancying his choice, had together ousted him from her presence. It was quite a mêlée, lasting the better part of a day. Garg had even returned the second day to do battle, scattering his rivals in a wild charge that left him for precious moments flanking the ripe she-fish.

But again, as before, his rivals re-formed their ranks and came at him crowding and butting, forcing him by weight of numbers to give ground. At last he could take no more. A madness seized him: an uncontrollable impulse to careen at breakneck speed through the marsh, forcing a path wherever his juggernaut bulk would take him: rooting, crushing, destroying, turning aside for no living thing. He was Garg. He and he alone ruled the shallow water domain of which he and his tribe had taken possession. He must make that fact abundantly clear.

Seldom, in recent years, had Garg's supremacy been questioned. For he was a huge fish of perhaps forty pounds in weight. This immense mass of flesh was shaped like a meat platter: deep and only slightly rounded, but thick through. With his high back and bulging nape he was perfectly suited to act the battering ram. Even his scales abetted the purpose. They were of a size to give the illusion of having been laid on with a trowel, like bricks, except that they were circular in shape, and flat. And they had a brassy look which, in their overlapped arrangement, gave the appearance of armour-plate.

Garg had no teeth, a deficiency common to the carp family. But, as his food consisted chiefly of insects and vegetation, the lack was not a handicap. What might seem further disadvantages were actually special adaptations to his particular feeding habits: a mouth hardly bigger than that of a perch, and a pair of fleshy barbels that dangled, one on each side of his lower jaw, like worms. With his mouth rounded to an O he could suck in food as a vacuum cleaner sucks in dust. The barbels were dual-purpose organs of perception, being lined with taste buds as well as highly sensitive to touch.

Garg's madness was almost certain to lead to his death. One possibility was that he would so spend his energy as to fall victim eventually to the snapping turtles that frequented the marsh, or to a watchful heron. The greatest danger he faced was of running aground somewhere in the flooded areas beyond the normal reaches of the marsh. For the spring run-off had not yet subsided. And weekly, the rains of an unusually wet May had added to the flood conditions.

Once in the danger area, his momentum might very well carry him onto dry land where, helpless, he would heave and struggle until he grew still and the birds came to peck at his eyes.

It is neither of these pitfalls, as it turns out, that entraps the disappointed suitor.

Above the water the bur reeds bend and fall back in sometimes straight, sometimes zigzag paths, marking the crazy gyrations of his flight. Now, in their choked midst, he reaches an impasse and blindly flails the wiry bars of his temporary prison until it appears that a buffeting wind has assailed the spot. Soon, however, he is off in the direction of deep water, appearing minutes later on the fringe of the rushes or in the desolate pools between the mounds of chokeweed.

Wherever his bull-like charges take him, his path remains visible long afterward. For the silt clouds settle but slowly.

And the weed-tunnels formed by his hurtling bulk take even longer to disappear.

Companies of springtails spring up all at once as he goes, like spray. A bittern, alarmed to see the sail-like back fin bearing down on it, leaps, all wings and beak, into the air, sounding its feelings in a throaty squawk. Coots and gallinules, surprised in hiding behind the still sere cattail blades, stride hastily off over sparse surface vegetation or flutter awkwardly to safer cover.

Now, all at once, Garg blunders into an unseen projection. It is large, like a log; heavy, as well; at the same time, soft and yielding.

Several times he has run full tilt into underwater branches, floating bog islands, and the like. His hump is raw from the battering. The velvety green of his back is marred by numerous scrapes and scratches, all injuries of a minor nature.

The impact on this occasion all but stuns him. Momentarily it unbalances the other party in the collision: Ma-Kee. She has been dozing, having, not long after daylight, bolted two of the spawning carp. Otherwise she would have been warned by Garg's clumsy approach.

Backing off, Garg's pig eyes follow the recoiling form of the muskellunge. Ordinarily he would have fled in terror at the sight. But his madness, coupled with this tangible evidence of his might, gives him a false notion of his chances in battle.

Ma-Kee has still not gathered herself when the bull carp's bulk bears down on her again, this time purposely. He is far from being a formidable antagonist except in size. But he has the advantage of being almost perfectly compacted, like a projectile. Besides, his opercles, thrust wide, have dangerous cutting edges. And his dorsal spine towers stiletto-fashion in a stiff spike.

Unable to swing her jaws into position in time, Ma-Kee once more suffers the indignity—and hurt—of his blow. It sends her reeling as though struck with a club. And Garg, following up, bulldogs the big muskellunge, butting and shoving her until, losing balance altogether, she rolls over and over, revealing intermittently the glistening white of her underside.

Wild boar and panther might so have fought. And for hectic, churning, tumbling moments, with Garg, dark and razor-backed, towering above Ma-Kee's sinuous length, the combatants bear a physical resemblance to those animal counterparts.

The sun provides bright stage-lighting for the drama. There is no audience, however. For the marsh, particularly since the carp had come, often resounded with the splashings of big fish. The skirmish now taking place, therefore, is of no more than passing interest to the creatures around. As long as they are not endangered, they can afford to remain unconcerned.

Ma-Kee is quickly free of her hapless state.

Thrusting frantically with fins and tail, at a moment when Garg overshoots her prostrate body, she manages a surging, half-slithering leap that takes her part way out of the water. When she comes down, she is far enough from Garg to permit her to recover balance completely and swing to meet his renewed onslaught.

Now the tables are turned. Garg, despite his size, seems pitifully defenceless as her steam-shovel jaws await his charge. It is not, however, a state of affairs to her liking, for her best offence is in attack. And in this engagement she is required to do battle while simply standing ground. But this time, at least, she is ready.

Her jaws clamp on Garg's head as a football player tackles an oncoming ball-carrier. His weight drives her back despite her braced fins. But her hold is secure and there is little else to do but wait.

The madness in Garg's brain is replaced by a sickening fear. He is now paying the penalty for his rashness. The pressure on his head is almost more than he can bear. One of his gill covers is jammed shut, requiring him to double his breathing rate. Ma-Kee's teeth have pierced an eye which, from beneath the enveloping gristle of her jaws, runs gore.

His combined pain and fright produce an even greater frenzy than had resulted from his madness. Back and forth he surges, carrying the big muskellunge with him. They can hardly be seen now because of the muck and debris stirred up in the battle. But presently, as Ma-Kee nears exhaustion, Garg's wild threshings quieten. Her jaws have done their job.

With difficulty she releases Garg's form. Like a capsized dreadnought, suffering the wounds of war, he sinks, all copper-scaled and lacerated, to the bottom, where he lies on his side feebly breathing. The horny plates of his cheeks are crushed. One torn branchiostegal ray trails like a remnant of undigested food. His mouth is lopsided, and his remaining eye rides high above its socket, from which it had been squeezed.

Had she been hungry, Ma-Kee would have devoured Garg, big as he was, at least partially. But she has fed well, and at the moment she wants no more.

The coming of the carp had been a mixed blessing. To predator fish, such as Ma-Kee, they represented a new food. Small carp abounded, providing plump fare for hungry mouths. And year after year there would be fresh crops to replace those that had grown beyond forage size.

The mischief they had wreaked, however, far exceeded this isolated benefit. The continual passage of their clumsy bodies, in and out, back and forth, through the rice and grasses, had given the marshland a disordered look. Bent and broken plants were everywhere, while whole areas of rice had been dislodged by the intruders' grubbing and rooting. This same hoglike practice had seen the disappearance of much of the underwater vegetation. For the marsh waters were now perpetually infiltrated with silt. Thus robbed of sunlight, the weeds could but struggle feebly or die.

It was a puzzle to many how the carp had come to be in the lake-chain. Due to its higher elevation, the Lakeland stood aloof from the larger carp-frequented waters below, and for many years had remained free of the invaders. Some thought that anglers, using carp minnows for bait, were responsible for the introduction; others that the unwanted fish had gained ingress via the locks. A more likely reason involved a commercial carp pond that at one time had been operated on one of the upper lakes. Rumour had it that, not many years before, the pond had gone out during a storm. Before the dam could be repaired, most of the stock had escaped.

In view of the size of many of the carp that began to appear through the lake system, it was quite likely that the carp pond was the source. Only breeder stock, carefully maintained, could account for such large specimens. Garg, probably, had been one of these.

Leaving Garg, Ma-Kee swims slowly to a comfortable resting place where the sun can blaze full down upon her. Lying there, she is the size and proportions of a shoal shark. Her heart is even more murderous.

What fisherman, spying her, would not find his throat go dry, his feet unsteady?

About her, instead of the vegetation she knows so well, are land grasses and plants, revealing that she has passed the boundary of the marsh and is in the inundated area surrounding it. But the water covers her by several inches, so she feels safe enough.

At a distance, as she lies there, some boys appear on the scene. There are four in all, one in hip waders, the other three with their trousers rolled up. They plan to chase the carp, which they know are in the shallows. It is a game, and they laugh and shout as all of a sudden they surprise a fish and rush after it, darting and splashing in this direction and that, attempting to cut it off from deeper water.

For all that it is a game, it has its serious side. Two of the boys carry sticks of a weight and shape to act as clubs. The boy in hip waders, the oldest of the four, is armed with a spear, which he has come by in some devious manner and in which he takes much pride. So far, since it has come into his possession, it has contributed to few kills. The reason is that, for the most part, he hurls it like a javelin, taking delight in the misses as well as the hits. Should he corner a fish, however, he has a fair chance of sinking the tines home.

The boys with the sticks also delight in flinging them after their fleeing targets, sometimes in frustration, mostly for the sheer fun of doing so. But even these ordinarily ineffectual weapons can deal death. A bewildered carp, run aground, is set upon and clubbed before being booted or dragged onto high land. Later, depending on their mood, they will either abandon their victims or haul them off home in a sack in the forlorn hope of finding a buyer.

Now a second mound of water spews through the grasses at right angles to the first, and further ecstatic shouts go up. Two carp! Alas, the new diversion is calamitous, for it splits their ranks. The tag-end boy, almost frothing with laughter and excitement like a shaken bottle of pop, goes charging off after the second fish, to be followed a moment later by his nearest companion who inwardly rails at his inability to run in two directions, but chooses the direction likely to yield the most action.

Veering, the first fish luckily finds itself in a deep depression, where its progress is more difficult to detect. The spear is thrown without luck. And, forced back by deep water, the two breathless pursuers give up. The second fish, similarly, proves too elusive. But what matter? Water and prospects aplenty lie ahead. So on with the chase!

They decide to work as close to the marsh as they can without getting a soaking, moving in a semi-circle as hunters often do in a rabbit drive. They will thus have a better chance both of spying fish and of cutting off their escape.

A wave, starting up suddenly at the edge of a large saucer-like area in their path, catches the boys' eyes at once. It is, they think, the movement caused by a pair of carp—perhaps several—lying together. But when they see it continue in one direction, they talk excitedly to one another, hazarding guesses as to what kind of a monster fish they have surprised.

One of the boys has glimpsed a streak of blotched grey. It looked, he thought, like an eel. Only no eel could possibly be so large. It looked even a bit like pictures he had seen of sharks.

"Go on!" the oldest boy admonished scathingly. "It's just a big old carp. Couldn't be anything else." But his heart pumped nevertheless as he noted the wake left by the mysterious quarry. And it was with some misgivings that he gave the order to proceed.

Caution was to be their watchword. With so huge a prize at stake there could be no missteps.

As yet, Ma-Kee is not alarmed. Misled by the comforting depth of water in the gully, it is not clear to her that she is swimming landward. A moment later, as her belly touches bottom, she senses the truth. It is as though a trigger has been pressed or a fuse fired, starting a projectile on its way. Off she darts toward the far side of the depression, creating something in the nature of a tidal wave in her going.

Her head, long and grim-snouted, can be clearly seen. Tail and back fin, protruding for a fleeting moment, seem separated by yards from the ghastly jaws.

At the sight, the boys fall back in terror.

"I told you it was a shark!" the one boy challenged, dry-lipped.

His companions look at each other, not speaking, knowing the claim to be false but having no counter-claim to offer.

Their glances return to the water, which is calm again. They can barely make out where the big fish lies, for Ma-Kee is once more in the deeper part of the depression and there will stay until disturbed. Gradually, adjusting themselves to the situation, their fears leave them and they begin to plot how they may trap the big fish.

The entrance to the saucer-like area is also the only exit. It is not wide. If only they can block it so the fish cannot get out . . .

Looking around, they spy a log. Posting the smallest member of the group to keep watch, the others step as carefully as they can to the spot. But their efforts to move the log are in vain. It is too heavy.

The spear-wielder then makes the decision. While the others block the entrance, he will approach the fish from the opposite direction and attempt to spear it.

The proposal seems rash. But what else is there to do? And so, their fear suddenly returning, his companions take their stand. All now are armed, for the smallest boy too has found a club with which to do battle.

Slowly, gingerly, the spear-wielder moves closer to Ma-Kee, wishing mightily all the while that he might abandon the project. But his greatest concern is for his own self-respect. He would lower himself in the eyes of the others should he give up now.

He can picture the moment when he will let fly the spear. But as matters turn out, it does not leave his hand.

Ma-Kee has had enough of disquiet. With a great thrust of tail that almost empties the spot of water, she bolts toward the entrance. Her now sharpened senses tell her that in that direction lies freedom. Not even the presence of the man creatures deters her.

She is not certain that they are in her path, for the grass hides the boys' legs. But by the noise of their splashings she knows they are close.

The splashings now grow in volume as the boys, seeing the huge fish almost on them, are seized with panic and frantically endeavour to get clear of its path. The spear-wielder, likewise panic-stricken, stands rooted to the place where he had flushed the monster, able only to shout wild warnings.

The bent bloated images of the man creatures soar above Ma-Kee. Their white stump-legs seem everywhere about her, confusing her, and in the rush she strikes one. There is a loud bursting sound, reaching her like distant thunder; followed by sudden intensified splashing. But she is past the entrance and pays the disturbance little heed.

Shortly, the murky waters of the marsh swallow her up.

Later that day two men, one armed with a baseball bat,

the other with a ·22 rifle, visit the flooded area. They are accompanied by three of the boys, who hang together behind the men and, when called upon, repeat over and over with sundry gesticulations the account of the happenings that had fetched their fathers to see how much of truth lay behind the story of the monster fish.

The fourth boy was a casualty and unable to come. He had been knocked down and attacked, according to the story. And indeed there was proof, for his leg was badly torn. Ma-Kee's opercle, rough-edged, like shale, had acted like a saw on the tender flesh.

It was enough to impress the adults who, although noting the absence of teeth marks, were forced to admit there was something strange about the whole affair.

They found no trace of the monster. But the episode was one of a growing number that caused wild rumours to circulate among the lake people and daily made Ma-Kee's existence more precarious.

Spring Kill

THERE followed a winter first of bitter cold, then of heavy snow. The ice roof that now imposed rigid penance on the once carefree lake surface thickened to a depth of many feet, robbing the lake inhabitants of much valuable living space. It robbed them, too, of something they could even less afford to lose: the oxygen that the down-driving air column above could no longer send into its depths.

Had the ice remained clear, no great harm would have been done. For there were the weeds—tentative acres of salvation—which, when acted upon by the sun's rays, themselves gave forth the life-sustaining element. But with the heavy snow layer perpetrating a reign of darkness, the normally friendly weed forests excreted poisonous gases instead.

Deep holes were scarce and usually appropriated by the largest fish. Thus it was that Ma-Kee suffered not a whit during most of the time of the shadow, having, owing to the size and depth of the retreat in which she had ensconced herself, plenty of living space and, most of all, plenty of water in which to breathe.

Food—what she needed of it in these months of slow digestion—she could easily get by occasional sorties into shallower areas. Yes, life even in such restricted circumstances was, for the strong, a matter of comparative luxury. And when, driven by the growing need for oxygen, smaller fish of all kinds began to venture into her quarters, she at first welcomed the invasion. To have delicacies of such a varied nature delivered to her very jaws! Fortune was being more than friendly to her.

This was all very well until the day arrived when she found that to breathe freely in the midst of her imminent victims was becoming increasingly difficult. That day she went berserk, scattering the uninvited company with fitful charges. Those that moved too slowly she seized and dropped in almost the same movement, paying no heed to the wreckage of crushed, bleeding bodies that fell everywhere around her.

Her last tormentor chased from the arena, she sank to the ooze floor panting heavily. A tinge of red suffused the baleful yellow of her eyes. Her lithe body, reptilian in the semi-darkness, lay slightly off balance and for a while it was an effort for her to keep from losing control and turning on her side.

Before long she had recovered, only to find that already many of the company she had put to flight were returning. This show of audacity in lesser creatures such as bass and perch which would ordinarily have given her wide berth was, even in her weakened condition, too much of an affront. Once again she wheeled on the invaders, who scattered obediently. But it was a losing battle. For, minutes after, driven by force of necessity, they were back.

Not even the presence of such an old she-dragon as Ma-Kee could keep them away.

Clearly, she would have to forsake the lair that had served her so well. Her gill surfaces, sensitive extractors of the water's life-gases were, combined, many times the area of those of her largest co-tenant. Her wants could brook no competition.

It is April. Far back in the bushland, the creeks—ebony veins in the snow-fleshed earth—are singing. Spring is fast approaching. But the ice will hold for weeks yet.

Ma-Kee moves like a bird dog on scent, feathery gill surfaces wide-flared, seeking the least hint, the slightest suspicion, of water more life-giving than that which she has left.

Where to?

The spillway at the upper end of the lake might well have summoned her. There, despite reduced winter draw-off, some water usually remained open. But she has no fondness for dams.

For succour she turns to the marsh where she was born. Often the hollow stalks of bur reeds form breathing tubes to the surface. Here and there, amid the cattail clusters, fine perforations in the ice crust become modest air holes.

But will the marsh admit her?

She is in luck. The first run-off, seeping into the marsh areas of the lake as though into vast sprawling sponges, has reduced the thickness of the ice layer. It is possible, she finds, to scout for air holes with relative ease. And when she finds one at last, she rests, luxuriating in the new life that fills her veins, not at all irked by the fact that, in exchange for this mercy, she must submit to the discomfort of being sandwiched between ice and bottom.

Still she knows her haven must be looked upon as temporary. She cannot stand such confinement for long. And so, when her respirations have returned to her usual rate (it is thirty-two per minute), she moves off under the ice, nosing away sunfish and minnow throngs as she goes: appearing, in the immensity of her body, in the grim line of her jaws, in eyes rimmed with cold fire, like some hobgoblin of the fish world.

Somewhere in the marsh there must be the ideal combination to suit her needs of the moment: air and space.

Unknown to Ma-Kee another hobgoblin is in the marsh. Cheeka, her old enemy, similarly impelled by a need for oxygen, has sought and found a refuge. It is a hole, perhaps a half-acre in extent, bordered on the land side by the bent and broken forms of bur reeds in such clusters that an almost perpetual in-draught of oxygen is provided. On the other side lies a shallow sand shoal: the white spot that perch fishermen look for. Because, later, when the surrounding weed-masses have regenerated, this would be a regular haunt of many high-backed perch.

It had been quite a squeeze for Cheeka to negotiate the area of water between ice ceiling and shoal. But she had managed it. And, having taken note of the suitability of what was to be her new quarters, she quickly set about to empty the area of its inhabitants—via the three-foot route from her throat to her stomach: the most convenient and satisfying method she knew.

If Ma-Kee is an apparition, Cheeka is almost equally so. Despite her years, which are more than Ma-Kee's, she has a tendency to slimness, making her head seem huge. This same tendency causes her underjaw to be singularly upthrusted as though, driven by the exigencies of hunger, she has on more than one occasion made half-hearted attempts to swallow herself.

To have escaped thus far with her life, even as Ma-Kee, in a world where danger lurked daily, above and below, testified to her cunning. It testified also to her strength. As yet, she has not tasted defeat. A June bug spinner, relic of her most recent encounter with a man creature, dangles from a corner of her lower jaw. (Fortunately, the single hook inconvenienced her but little.) And she has actually bested an otter in combat, as formidable an opponent as she is likely to meet.

Ma-Kee, in the frenzy of her search for a refuge big enough to accommodate her, chances on Cheeka's retreat. Water currents set up by her entry into the hole bring Cheeka to see with what new food item she is being provided. In the gloom, neither at once recognizes the other. But the encouragement of recognition is not needed for attack.

A meeting, thunderous in all its tumultuous aspects save sound. Ribbons of green-tinged water flee the massive bodies. Above them the surface heaves in a sudden great welling that threatens to crack the already weakened ice sheet.

Cheeka charges head on, preferring to put her powerful mandibles to test in a jaw-to-jaw duel. But Ma-Kee, sly old tussler that she is, has other plans,

Seeming ready to meet her opponent's challenge, at the last second she swerves, eel-like, selecting as her target the vulnerable zone safely beyond Cheeka's powerful mandibles where gill plates end and scale-layered flesh begins.

In the very energy of her flight she misses. Hurtling over and past Cheeka's serpentine form, she still manages to use teeth to advantage, ripping a raw streak in her adversary's back—a minor score in the deadly game, but the first. And while the dislodged scales, caught as though in a wind, swirl in tiny light-flecked paths through the debris-laden water, Cheeka returns the hurt.

From her position underneath, she has seized Ma-Kee between anal and tail fins. Not long does she maintain this awkward hold. Though drawing blood, she is quickly flung loose and both fish fall back, almost immediately to collide again.

Jaw clamped on jaw the two fish tumble over and over in a colourless kaleidoscope of grey and white, powerful tail fins whisking up mud and weed in the manner of an oarsman whose boat has become mired. It is impossible now to see. In this circumstance comes a lull in the battle during which, as though by consent, they both release their holds.

Except for the teeth marks in the area above her tail, Ma-Kee has suffered little damage. Not so Cheeka. The vision is gone from one of her eyes where Ma-Kee's incisor had embedded. This puts them on more even terms. For the eye that Krark's beak had set askew had not served Ma-Kee properly since.

It is this turn of events that sees the finish of the fray.

Ma-Kee has had enough of waiting. She is impatient for the kill. And when the water clears to reveal again the gaunt shape of her rival she moves in on Cheeka's blind side.

With monstrous relish, she now has Cheeka by the belly. A vigorous shaking, and suddenly her jaws have torn a great chunk from Cheeka's underside. The torn flesh still in her jaws, she watches without emotion as the feebly writhing body of Cheeka sinks slowly to the bottom.

Why should she be further interested? This sort of thing has been the daily substance of her life.

The ice break-up is now very close. Its imminence brings peril to Ma-Kee; needless death to many of her fellows.

From the height at which Pandion the osprey soon will recommence his ceaseless patrol, the Lakeland is a vista of natural lakes, once linked by waterfalls.

To the men who operate the dams that now replace the waterfalls, the lakes are a series of reservoirs. In their pulse-less view, the water is impounded solely for navigation and waterpower. Only incidentally is it a repository of fish life, and to the aquatic populations they pay little heed.

At the lower dam of the lake where Ma-Kee lies in refuge, officials decide to draw off water while the ice is still on. "Flood control," they later called it. But the freshet was weeks away. And with the far-swinging areas of shoreline to take up excess water, floods had never been a danger in the Lakeland.

Overnight the water dropped. In forty-eight hours, several feet had been taken.

Ma-Kee, in her pool, was landlocked. So too were many other muskellunge which, like Ma-Kee, had sought out pockets in the marshes where they could breathe more freely. But, unlike Ma-Kee, they had little depth of water to shelter them, and so were quickly exposed.

The noise, under the ice, of dying fish, was as the noise of fish in a huge net that has been drawn ashore. When the ice went out soon after, dead muskellunge littered the exposed areas of the marsh. Only Ma-Kee, in her isolated basin, is left alive.

That same day a muskrat trapper, scouring the marsh for likely sets, stands aghast at the slaughter. The mud so handicaps his progress it is with difficulty that he secures several specimens to take with him as evidence. While doing so, he passes close to the landlocked hole where Ma-Kee lies confined. Startled by his shadow, she bolts to the far end of the hole, the force of her going churning up the torn body of Cheeka.

Now it is the trapper's turn to be startled. He stares in disbelief at the scene, trying to connect the conflicting events that meet his eyes and ears: the disturbance, surely caused by a creature of great size and strength, and the sudden entry into his view of a dead muskellunge of huge proportions— obviously the victim of an opponent even larger and stronger.

Ma-Kee is not visible. And the trapper has no wish to go closer.

At length, knowing he has no choice, he decides to leave. On the morrow he will return, armed with a shotgun. Then he will be better prepared to investigate.

That night during a heavy rain, sensing her opportunity, Ma-Kee leaves the pool. Her sense of direction does not fail her. She covers half the distance between pool and lake in a surging leap. Now her broad tail and straining body must do the rest.

Half slithering, half jumping, she negotiates the remaining distance. When, at last, water bathes her gills, she knows she is free.

News of the needless killing of the muskellunge brought violent criticism. Back in the cities, newspapers turned a spotlight on the affair.

ANGLERS PROTEST MUSKELLUNGE MASSACRE
ILL-TIMED CANAL RUN-OFF KILLS THOUSANDS
OF FISH

So ran the headlines. But the protest had little effect. Canal authorities sympathized but argued that their concern was maintenance of water levels, not maintenance of fish populations. Besides, canals were a federal matter. They were beyond local criticism.

When the news reached the biologists who had worked so long on the muskellunge project, they looked at one another.

"What a joke!" one exclaimed bitterly. "On us. We rear one muskie. They kill a thousand."

But the worst was to come. Concerned only with the mechanics of canal operation, the ruthless scheme was continued. At a later date, when the muskellunge were far inland spawning following heavy rains, the dams again did their deadly work.

Almost overnight, spawning areas were denuded. Eggs, dropped and fertilized by the spawning fish just days before, now lay clustered, dry and lifeless, amid the exposed bottom vegetation.

A fresh outcry greeted this new misfortune. But it was feebler, and short-lived. For the evidence was not as easily seen. And besides, dead eggs are not as shocking as dead fish.

In the district, the tragedy became known as spring kill. Spring, which ordinarily gave forth life, had given forth death in its stead.

Ma-Kee, abroad after her sojourn in the marshes, looked only ahead. She might well look cautiously. For, adding to the alarming tales of a lake monster, the trapper had told his story. The hue and cry was on.

The Man-Threat

BY day and by night now, Ma-Kee's life is in danger. In the early spring, darkness cloaked the activities of poachers. Some cruised the shallows with spears, newly fashioned or rusted with disuse, never knowing what paddle stroke would find the monster before them, illumined in the pale light of lantern or cresset. Others, seized with the same illegal zest, stayed the night by fires, fishing with handlines in an effort to lure her as they would lake trout.

There was even secret talk, among the villagers, of nets and dynamite as means of taking her. And who was to say that such devices were not tried? For there was only Moses Todd to keep watch. And the potential malefactors were many.

With the arrival of the fishing season, anglers came to the lake in greater numbers, hopeful of hooking the giant fish. Recognizing her as a tourist attraction, the local newspaper offered a prize for her capture.

But still she is not caught.

She is saved from a sudden end only because the lake is broad, and because her inclination on most occasions now is to put many feet of water over her head. The depths of the lake swallow her for weeks at a time. Far down in a muffled grey-green world she lies. Above, unseen and unheard, the boats ply the watery paths in vain search of her.

A west wind can summon her from her dungeon lair. So too can the urge to visit her favourite marshes with their weed-thronged shallows where even one of her vast bulk can doze out the sunlit hours undisturbed.

These temptations several times almost prove her undoing.

A day when summer is a shimmering pendulum, for the moment stilled, finds Ma-Kee in the marsh. She lies close to shore, so placed amid the vegetation that all that may be seen of her from above is her back. Her murderous head is hidden from view by the sheltering leaves of Castalia, the pond lily. Her tail, a good four feet away, is gently imprisoned in a morass of hornwort.

A farmer, spying her motionless form, is at first unable to believe his eyes. This surely is the fish about which all the stories have been told. The chance is his to capture it. But how?

From where he stands, peering through the rush screen, it is but a few minutes to his barn, for his meadow runs to the very edge of the marsh. Cautiously he withdraws and, with an alacrity that leaves him breathless, returns with the first weapon at hand: a manure fork. With this raised, he steals upon her.

The old fish, peacefully dreaming, is unaware of danger. The sun, overhead, casts no shadow. The farmer, realizing that only the greatest luck and agility will deliver his prize to him, treads with scheduled precision. . . . Only a step or two now and he will be within striking distance.

But Ma-Kee is not so old as not to have all her wits about her. And her stalker's progress through knee-deep water must inevitably rouse her from lethargy.

Her going, when the moment comes, is with the suddenness of a bomb-burst. In the cauldron of muck and weed formed by her departure, the farmer sees her head. A fleeting glimpse only, but the awesome sight affects his aim.

Striking wildly, steel tines down-driven with malicious purpose, he misses by more than a foot. But he comes within inches of skewering his own leg.

Later that same day Ma-Kee did bring about the release of blood not her own into the waters of the marsh.

The cedar swamp behind the marsh is the home of many deer. In the late afternoon a doe and a fawn emerge from the swamp to browse on the tender marsh grasses. Having had their fill, they now pick dainty ways through the green profusion of arrowheads and bur reeds, coming to a stop where the duckweed has spilled like green paint onto the shore.

All, apparently, is safe. And so the fawn continues out into the marsh waters where, at the nearest pool, it will drink. Golden ripples flee the stilt-like legs, now disappearing amid the purple fringes of the spatterdock, now emerging in the glassy water stretches to set the white cloud images trembling.

The borrowed splendour of evening, spreading its extravagant dyes over the whole vast acreage of marsh, camouflages and renders indistinguishable the ominous shadow that now moves upon the scene.

A frightened bleat is the first indication that something is amiss. This is followed by the violently protesting struggles of the fawn as it is dragged into deep water.

A canoeist, happening to focus his attention on the animals from a distance, was hard put to explain the event.

"The animal appeared to be fighting for its life," he described it later to a knot of listeners. "I can't credit there was anything big enough in that marsh to pull it under. But what can you think?" What, indeed, could one think?

It was the monster again, they decided. One among them took note of the exact location of the happening. He was a man who had long sought the big fish; a lean pipe-smoking man with a bent high-ridged nose that seemed always to be testing the strength of its taut skin-casing, who summered for months at a time on a promontory overlooking the lake.

"The eagle in his eyrie," the villagers often remarked mockingly when they saw him seated on his cabin stoop high in the distance.

And they had double reason so to describe the beak-nosed man. For he swooped down on unwary trespassers as would a bird of prey on a field mouse. But he was known to be a fisherman of cunning. And no one was surprised to hear him declare that the big fish was his special target.

He was in no hurry. And once having journeyed the distance to the marsh to mark well the nature of the water, he let matters rest. If the fish had visited the marsh area once, it would do so again. But the heavens were not right. A seafarer in his youth, his life was still partially charted by the stars. When the sun had edged into Libra and a hint of autumn was in the air would be time.

Meanwhile—with a price on her head—Ma-Kee was back in her deep-water lair. In due course she had given up her attempts to gorge the awkward creature she had captured. The incident, so far as she was concerned, ended there.

She could not know that it had brought her a special enemy, an enemy whose guile matched her own. And that the time for testing was not far off.

August kindled summer's flame to searing whiteness. In the waters of the lake there was seldom movement unless it was to seek the haven of shadow. Pale columns of sunlight thrust deep into the weeds, revealing them to be without mystery. Only the deepest channels maintained a cloak of secrecy. And there, for the most part, Ma-Kee was content to lie.

Even though some days saw thick cloud covering the heavens, she still had little inclination to forsake her retreat. For the surface waters were suffocatingly warm. But while she might be inactive, her enemy in his distant eyrie was not.

With great patience he has managed to catch and confine, uninjured, a number of large suckers. A lift of a draw net in a small bay adjoining the promontory's lower slope will, at any time, bring them dark-backed and squirming into his presence. From there they can quickly be transferred to the metal-lined well in his punt.

On shore, he has assembled half a dozen two-gallon tins of the type used for turpentine. All of these are empty, tightly corked and painted green. To each is attached a length of the heaviest line he could buy. And this too he has rendered green by soaking in cuprinol.

When the time arrives he will have hooks in keeping. Already he has selected them for size and strength. It but remains to touch up their points. In his mind's eye he can see himself setting his giant floats free upon the water. He has not used this trick since he was a boy, and he anticipates the moment excitedly. It is as well that autumn is required to set the stage. By then there will be few on the lake to spy on his activities.

On a chill night many weeks later, as the man sits in his cabin, the sound comes to his ears. At first it is a low singing, dying out to a muttering. Now the singing begins again, suddenly increasing in volume, breaking off into many cadences. Then silence.

Rising from his chair he darkens the room and opens the door to look out upon the night. In the open doorway he meets the sound again. The singing increases to a fierce intensity and he perceives that it comes from the topmost branches of the tall pines that now appear to be but black gatherings upon the hill. The singing is so shrill that he is hardly conscious of the buffeting noise in the background, like great muffled drum beats.

Then the singing stops again and the buffeting becomes a rumbling that seems to emerge from the whole great throat of night. The man smiles and closes the door. This is the signal he has been awaiting.

Before he goes to bed, the wind goes *whewww* as its singing increases to full measure. Then *whoo-whoo* as it breaks into gusty blasts. It will be a two-day blow, he is sure. The giant fish will be imprisoned. And when the equinoctial force has been spent, the days will be colder. That is when his long-sought prey will be on the move.

Out from the marsh area on a morning following the blow, one by one, over a quarter-mile extent, he sets his floats. To each is hooked a sucker of a pound or more in weight. Then, binoculars in hand, he cruises at a distance.

Floating free, the tins cover much water. When one has drifted too far he must retrieve it, examine the bait, then set it adrift again in the selected area.

He has cunningly reasoned that the big fish may well lie in the deep water nearest the marsh. And so he has charted his fishing beat to take in the entire territory. Whether Ma-Kee remains in her retreat or chooses the occasion to visit the marsh there is the chance she will see one of the offerings. It is a test of patience. He may have to repeat the procedure for days on end. And even then there is no certainty that his plot will succeed.

But he is in luck. On the afternoon of his second attempt, Ma-Kee rises to the bait. She is on it in a rush, engulfing the sucker as though it was a minnow and bolting it in successive gulps. It is only as she moves off that she feels the resistance of the float. But she drags it under regardless.

With a start, the man in the boat realizes what has happened. The bait was of a size that would attract only a very large fish. He was prepared for such a fish to take. But a fish that could drag a two-gallon tin under water!

He had been shivering, for the day is sharp, as he had anticipated. Now a high pitch of excitement warms him.

He looks out across the water to where he had last seen the tin. There is no turmoil. No sign of a struggle. A sickening thought assails him. Of course! In some way the cork had come loose: the tin had simply filled with water and sunk. But as he gears his motor to investigate, of a sudden the tin surfaces again and a new wave of excitement sweeps over him.

There was now no doubt. A very large fish had taken the bait.

For an hour or more he could not bring himself to go near. When he did, and glimpsed the monster his plot had hatched, he sank limply onto the seat. No one would believe such a fish existed. Yet there it was.

Ma-Kee, her strength partly exhausted, swam in full view, towing the tin as though in some capricious manner she had come by and was lofting a toy balloon. From gill cover to gill cover her head seemed a foot wide. Her ribbed jowls, standing out from the line of her immense body, caused her to look like some creature of another age. A single brassy eye exposed to his view was, for all its yellow fire, coldly hypnotic. How long would it be before he dared attempt to grapple with the monster?

His plan had been to tow fish and tin ashore. But all around were choked weed masses. The line would never stand such a test. And though he had a gaff aboard, he would not be such a fool as to try it.

A better plan came to him. The fish was plainly tired from its endeavours to sound. Try as it might, the Brobdingnagian float was too much for it. He would lift the tin aboard, thus forcing the fish to surface. Then, with the length of iron pipe he carried as a cudgel, he would stun it.

A quick lift and the tin was aboard, clattering to rest against the side. Now the cudgel. A crowding sensation in his chest seeming to smother him, he reached for the pipe. The great fish was alongside, apparently submissive.

But the man, more than ever in that moment the bird of prey, had reckoned without the vitality of the species with which he was in combat.

On that instant Ma-Kee rose in a desperate leap that thrust half her length above the surface of the water, revealing as she did so not merely the large treble hook she had only recently taken but rusted specimens of other adventures as well.

In alarm her pursuer shrank back. But too late to avoid her descending form. With a start of fear he felt the hooks pierce the collar of his sweater. Then, with the weight of her body pulling him, he was in the water. Simultaneously the line snapped under him as the tin jammed between oar and gunwale.

No such nightmare could have come to him in his most troubled sleep. The open jaws of the fish were even with his face. In the struggle, pain and blood blinded him. He reached for and found the gunwale. And hanging on with one hand, he shoved at the fish's snout with his free elbow. His efforts were sufficient to tear the hooks clear of his sweater. The turmoil subsided. The giant fish was gone. The nightmare was over.

When at length, exhausted, he managed to pull himself aboard, his face ran blood from half a dozen wounds, whether from hooks or teeth his dazed senses could not tell.

The villagers, to whom he felt obliged to reveal the truth because of the peculiar nature of his injuries, thenceforth had among them living evidence of the monster's existence. And they never failed to point the man out to visitors whenever the chance arose.

The wounds healed but scars took their place. Everyone said he was lucky.

Hope

ONE evening when a west wind romps like an animal in the shore grasses, an angler sits in his boat regarding not his float but a loon which he has called, with practised mimicry, from a distance.

Motionless, not daring even to lift his now cold pipe to his lips, he revels in the diversion. Maung, suspicious, head lofted like a conning tower, cruises not fifty yards from him. Never has he called a loon so close.

From his throat a soft tremolo—soothing, beckoning—a note or two only. Then the power to utter further sound forsakes him.

A sight putting the miracle of the loon out of thinking is in his eyes, to remain there later whenever he closes them and summons the vision to appear.

Maung, necklace adorned, one moment peripatetic, proud, kingly, riding the waves. Maung, next moment, to the accompaniment of a violent surge of water—pinioned in the jaws of a fish so large as to make the loon seem a duckling.

The angler has a glimpse of shining scale extending from one yawning gill cover to the other. And too—can he believe his senses?—unmistakably to his ears there comes the slight but positive sound of metal on metal: an instant only, tinny, faintly clanking. A suspicion. No—more than a suspicion.

How account for this remarkable sound? To the angler's mind comes recollection of the jest concerning fabled fish of fishermen's tales, so huge and so old that their scales were heard to rattle when they surfaced and shook themselves.

The last he sees of the scene as fish and bird swiftly sub-merge is Maung's head frantically striking at his captor.

The soot of night scatters slowly over land and lake. And with its coming he feels the desire to be anywhere but here in this watery wilderness, a desire that becomes translated into action as he lifts anchor and starts his motor.

Long after, his experience related to only a few close friends for fear of being laughed at, he is at a loss for an ex-planation. How could he know that the explanation was simple in the extreme?

A week before, Ma-Kee had made off with a double-blade trolling spoon. It was this, appended loosely to the unseen side of her upper jaw, that had made the curious noise. Thus was born still another tale about the giant muskellunge of the Kawarthas, embellished in each retelling, but containing enough of truth to cause fishermen to shake their heads in wonder.

In her great size and strength, in her awesome appearance and terrifying assaults, Ma-Kee was the reincarnation of the fabled fish whose scales rattled. She was the reincarnation also of all the other long line of fish that always got away, that were strong enough to tow boats or that frightened anglers into cutting the lines that held their monstrous quarry.

Her like was seen only occasionally nowadays, dragged up in nets from the bottoms of deep ship channels or taken in some wilderness lake where anglers seldom penetrated.

She now weighs more than seventy pounds. She is not the largest of her species ever recorded, but of a size to produce excited newspaper stories should she be caught. Her diet is supplemented increasingly with muskrats, water-fowl and other surface-swimming creatures. These she prefers because of their size and because they are easily captured.

Food items such as a six-pound pickerel are common fare. Seized, turned, and greedily worked head first through the teeth-studded cavern to the fateful folds of her swallowing sac, the victim, tail feebly flailing the water a foot beyond its captor's snout, now must face the final torture of suffocation.

Which ordeal has been the worst? Only the victim knows. Perhaps it was none of the steps pictured. The moment of the attack when Ma-Kee, out of all proportion to her surroundings, thunders in upon the intended victim's aura of consciousness, nightmare jaws held wide as though by some invisible prop, may well, by comparison, have paled all else.

A meal that would have satisfied one fisherman and his family has been downed at a gulp. Of course, it will last Ma-Kee several days. For mouth and craw are distended to bursting, and there is still more to swallow.

It was the fashion now for anglers to claim to have hooked her. Very often, his hook making fast in some underwater projection, the angler's face becomes strained. His broken line, retrieved in mingled relief and disappointment, he points to as evidence of the tremendous strike.

Every large muskie captured was claimed to be the monster, and the newspaper prize petitioned for. But the hopeful captors were made to run the gauntlet of critics who professed to have had first-hand encounters with the real monster, with the result that their claims usually brought quick rejection.

At the research project, news of each fresh exploit concerning the big muskellunge was met with jubilation. For Ma-Kee had been the means of drawing attention to the work they had carried on forlornly for so long.

With the publicity that surrounded Ma-Kee, newspapers began to recall the wanton destruction of muskellunge on the spawning beds and to take note of the increasingly poor catches of keeper fish.

"What a shame," they cried, "that this great species should be allowed to continue its downward trend! Our greatest tourist attraction. And we don't lift a hand to perpetuate it."

Tourist and outfitter groups took up the cry. Soon, with

the realization that salvation was perhaps already in their midst, attention fastened on the research project.

A sportsmen's show, operated on behalf of conservation, made the first of what were to be yearly grants to the project. The government department concerned with fisheries matters promised new buildings and the assistance of a full-time government biologist. As for water levels, transport officials agreed that draw-offs could be "less hasty," to the disadvantage of none and to the certain advantage of fish populations.

It would be a slow road. But already the future for Ma-Kee and her kind looked brighter.

September arrived—Moon of the Wild Rice. This was a time of activity for the Ojibways, and of celebration. For then the wild rice was harvested.

The rice was an important source of revenue for the Indians. The white man esteemed it as a delicacy, and because of its scarcity was willing to pay a high price to bring it to his table. Moreover, it was a crop that had neither to be sown nor cultivated.

Each year the Indians watched the progress of the rice with anxious eyes. Adverse weather could see the kernels fail to mature. Ill-timed winds could strip the flimsy stalks of their seed pods so completely that little would remain to harvest.

The wind was their greatest enemy. But this year the Great Spirit had smiled on them. The rice had weathered well. It had headed abundantly in July's steady heat; ripened during August. September's early winds had not molested it.

Now it stood in readiness, awaiting the onslaught of the Indians' picking-sticks, as green as the summer grasses, as luxuriant as the farmer's wheat and just as tall. It bristled at the mouths of creeks and in the shallow marsh areas. In some spots great beds, finding a fertile host in boggy lake bottom, seemed to run on forever.

On the first day of calm a flotilla set out from the reservation. A dozen canoes in all, each manned with a pusher and a beater. By prearranged plan the stands had been divided up. Thus the canoes before long began to head in different directions.

One by one they disappear into the rice. To the paddler in the prow falls the task of propelling his craft through the thick vegetation. His stout maple blade becomes an instrument with which to push as well as to paddle.

His companion, kneeling amidships, commences the work of harvesting. He wields his wand-like picking-sticks like a drummer, with one deftly catching and bending a mass of slender stalks inward, with the other gently tapping the rice heads into the canoe bottom.

One canoe, working a stand methodically back and forth, can harvest several acres in a day. There is no need to infringe upon another's territory. And as each boat for the most part represents one family, with the squaws in many cases acting as beaters, this is just as well.

Little Tom, paddle sometimes digging, sometimes pushing, sometimes forensically sparring with the rice to find suitable purchase, leans into the imminent stalks as though into a rain of hail. Through the slow hours of the day he thinks only of the task ahead and of the growing mound of green in the canoe bottom.

His nephew, still more boy than man, allows the steady tap-tap of his picking-sticks to lull him into visions of the harvesting's exciting aftermath. There will be food, of course, to celebrate. Much food. And dancing. And the men will sit smoking, tired after their efforts, recounting the day's events and discussing the likely market price of the rice.

Next, the pods will be parched over a fire to loosen the hulls. The boys of the reservation will then "dance the rice," pouring quantities into open pits in the ground and jumping up and down on the yielding mass until the hulls separate from the grain. Or perhaps the grain will be poured into cotton bags, these to be kneaded and pommelled and jumped upon. For this method was deemed the better.

And still the activity would not be over. There would remain the winnowing. Birchbark trays, to toss the rice into the air for the wind to catch and distribute the chaff, have already been fashioned and are in readiness.

There were many pauses in the canoe's progress, for the effort was great and an ache grew in Little Tom's arms. A long respite in the early afternoon when they ate their bread and salt pork. A still longer respite while Little Tom dozed where he sat, and dragonflies hovered and boat bugs soared, each in their separate voids, and the young Indian watched with impatient eyes the mosaic of checked shirt and weathered skin that was his elder.

Then once more to paddle and picking-sticks. They must stay with their work until the canoe can hold no more. Who could tell? Mon-e-doo might summon a wind that very night that would send the rice to the bottom.

The day was a pale image of its earlier splendour when they left the rice stand and headed for the reservation. True to Little Tom's conjecture a brisk wind had sprung up. It bade them be careful. Rice-laden, a matter of minutes could see them ship enough water to sink their craft under them, a threat not only to the fruit of their labours but to their very lives.

For perhaps half a mile they would be forced to traverse open water. Then the haven of a roundabout route that would thrust between them and the wind the protective bulk of a sprawling rocky island. Narrow channels at either end separated their bulwark of safety from the mainland. In between, the water widened into a long quiet bay.

It was a familiar route, used when the going was rough. By mutual agreement they would take to it that night. And now as he faced the lake with its expanse of silvered water and darkening tree-fringed shoreline Little Tom's thoughts turned to the mysteries that lay hidden from his eyes. The *kinonge*, Ma-Kee, as he had long before named the big she-fish, dwelt especially in his mind.

He was sure it was the same fish that the Baron, the angler he had guided years before, had hooked and lost—grown, of course, much larger. Would his eyes ever dwell upon it

again? It would not seem so, had he seriously considered the question. One could not after all expect Mon-e-doo to grant such a favour a second time.

And yet at that very moment events were shaping themselves to bring about that unlikely circumstance.

In the bay which they were shortly to enter, Ma-Kee lay, surfaced. To one side of her was a tangle of floating weed; on the other a pool of open water. It was a restful place and she was conscious of nothing save the blissful aftermath of a day of activity during which she had gorged herself on bullfrogs. This was the time of year when bullfrogs, driven from the swamps because of low water, thronged the shores and back bays of the lake. They were easy targets for her wolf-like leaps. Several she had taken, resting place and all, as they reposed in seeming safety on lily-pad pillows. She had not had such feeding in many weeks.

The canoe, ploughing cleanly ahead under the impetus of its burden and the sure steady strokes of Little Tom and his nephew, soon reached the channel entrance. Swiftly it bore down on the spot where Ma-Kee lay.

An excited shout now as, even in the fading light, the paddler in the prow spies the dark shape, dorsal and tail cleaving the surface like the distant sails of a foundering schooner.

Thinking herself trapped, Ma-Kee spurns the sea of weed. Her thunderous passage across the open pool is met by the on-charging canoe, only partially swerved off course by the frantic digging in of Little Tom's paddle.

Collision!

There is a moment of extraordinary happenings when fish, man and boy are all in the perilously tipping boat.

Ma-Kee's great rush has skidded her involuntarily over the edge of the low-riding craft, head reared, shimmering body soaring as though propelled by a spring. Now she collapses into the yielding rice, protesting this new environment with python agility even as the boy, screaming, protests the presence of the immense fish, and Little Tom, yielding to the inevitable, forgoes his attempts to keep the canoe upright and takes to the water.

Hardly does he find the shallow bottom with his feet before he finds that boy and fish have joined him.

A mighty swirl and Ma-Kee is free of the encumbering canoe. Seconds later, her wake still bubbling the surface, they are left alone. And there they stand in the darkness and numbing cold of the water, under the first winking stars, trying to gather their scattered wits. A veritable bog of rice is slowly deposited at their feet.

Successfully the canoe is righted, the paddles retrieved.

"A visitation arranged by the Great Spirit himself," the older man decides. Of what is it an omen?

At the reservation, when hot drinks and dry clothing have warmed them, their tale is told and retold.

It was the great event of Little Tom's life. He neither confirmed nor denied his nephew's version that the big fish had attacked them. He knew better. But it was true that the nephew attracted the largest knot of listeners.

The New Rod

THE boys emerged from the cedar thicket with the broad lake in full view: Mat in the lead, Sam following closely, chewing on a spike of timothy picked from the tame meadow on their way. Billy, Mat's younger brother, was still behind them; and Sam, hunching down to peer through an opening in the foliage, caught Billy's head, the blaze of the meadow, and the bunkhouse all in a glimpse.

"Let's go—Billy'll manage," said Mat. With these words, he continued on down over the hard, root-veined turf toward the water. He was thinking of Billy's fishing rod. Billy would be seeking all the easy ways out so as not to risk damaging it. Even then it would keep getting caught on things, or the lure would come loose from the reel as had happened often since they had left camp. He smiled.

On the shore, pulled well up, was the boat. It was square sterned, flat bottomed, with high gunwales. It had oars and a paddle. Mat and Sam went to it and shoved, one on each side of the prow, until it was launched, and then Billy finally appeared, managing, despite his tardiness, to be first aboard.

The day before, the boat had conveyed all three of them to the spot, a half-mile or so from their parents' cottages. Incessant entreaty had won them permission to camp out for a few days. They would live the life of woodsmen, they had decided when the scheme had first blossomed. They would snare rabbits. Catch fish. Cook their meals in the open.

A few rods from the lake, on the edge of the tame meadow, stood a sagging log building that had once been a stable when loggers operated in the district. With a little cleaning up it did very well as a bunkhouse, in a remote way befitting the woodsmen roles they had chosen to play. And from the tame meadow—distinct from wild meadows because it had been cultivated by the loggers to provide forage for their horses —the boys gathered armfuls of sweet-smelling grasses on which to lay their bedrolls.

Together they had toted in their supplies. In the matter of food there was a well-stocked basket specially for Billy : his mother had seen to that. But for themselves, Mat and Sam had brought only bare essentials : flour to make buns, bacon to supply cooking fat for the fish and rabbits they confidently expected to catch, salt, pepper, butter, canned milk and, for emergency, a few tins of stew.

"Those kids!" Mat's father had exploded laughingly. "Did you see the fish snare they had rigged up? About as much chance of getting anything with that as putting salt on partridge tails. Bet they'll be back for more grub before they're gone a day."

"Well, Billy has his new rod," demurred the mother.

And that is how it was as the boys pushed off in the boat. Billy, in sun hat and striped jersey, sat in the stern, looking welded, almost, to his new fishing rod, a birthday present from his father. Mat half kneeled, half sat in the bow, eager for the activity ahead. Tall for fourteen, he felt every bit the helmsman, twisting his dark, serious face every so often to give directions to his friend Sam at the oars.

It was Mat's responsibility to get the fish they needed for supper. Across the bow, grasped tightly in one hand, lay the device he had fashioned for the purpose, and that had brought so much amusement to his father. It was a fish snare, of the sort poachers used in England. He had seen it illustrated in a book and had duplicated it from memory. But time had erased all except the most meagre details from his mind. The resultant instrument, therefore, had none of the wand-like delicacy of the original. Instead of a pliant willow gad, Mat had used a clothes prop. The copper wire that was wound around one end of the prop, and continued below in a running noose, was of a heavier gauge than even the most naïve of poachers would have seen fit to employ.

But though the materials differed, the principle was the same. And Mat's thoughts lived out the time, not far off, when the snare would be put into action. There, in mind's eye, is spied the large fish lazing in the shallows. Carefully the noose is dipped into the water behind it. Ever so gently it is moved ahead until it encircles the quarry. Then, like lightning, the quick jerk that tightens the noose and at the same time lifts the surprised victim into the air.

"Can I? Can I, Mat?" His brother's voice interrupted his musings, harking hopefully back to a previous conversation. "While you're looking? I might get one."

"I told you before: No. Why do you think I made this snare?" Mat spoke impatiently, endeavouring, none too successfully, to invest his words with an air of finality. Real woodsmen who lived off the bush wouldn't have fancy fishing rods and reels, he thought with a touch of scorn. If they wanted fish, they'd rig up a throwline or make a snare like his.

There was another reason for his lack of encouragement. Billy's outfit was a sort of junior fishing outfit. The rod was short and stout, with red and white windings. The reel turned with a grinding sound. The line looked heavy enough to tow a barge. And the lure! . . . That funny-looking lure!

Mat stole a glance at the gaudy plastic affair dangling from Billy's rod tip. Billy had chosen it himself on his visit to the tackle store with his father. The body was yellow with red splotches. It had a propeller for a nose, and whitish, barley-striped eyes surrounded by gold paint. At sight of it, surely, a normally prudent fish would be apt to turn and run.

Sam, whose red hair belied his bland disposition, took up the conversation. "You see, Billy," he said, idling the oars, "suppose we were stranded. Suppose we had no rod or line or hooks. We'd just have to invent a way to catch fish."

"That's right," Mat lifted the prop proudly. "This is an

invention. It shows we have en-engin. . . ." The word eluded him. "Well, anyway—it'd prove we're not greenhorns. That we could live by our wits if we had to. Now try and forget your rod, Billy." Then, in a kinder tone, because he spied a quiver playing about his brother's lips: "Tell you—when we're done snaring, then you can try out your rod."

Billy's face brightened. "Promise?"

"Promise."

As the boat made lurching progress toward the back bay that was to be the scene of the snaring expedition, Billy's gaze travelled the length of his fishing outfit, coming to rest on the gaudy, many-hooked lure. He had his own ideas as to its merits.

Such a beautiful bait! When the time came, he knew it would catch fish.

That morning, Ma-Kee was late abroad. For a week, because of the enervating effect of the warm surface water, she had remained deep, feeding little. But today hunger nagged at her, urging her off the barren lake floor where only debris and such insignificant life-forms as mussels and red midge larvae kept her company.

As she swam upward at an angle through the half-light, the bottom rose, and weeds began to appear. When she had reached normal depth she found she could breathe quite well. The water was cooler, the result of a recent wind change. An agreeable sense of well-being filled her. This increased her appetite. But not her luck.

A school of large perch, not at once recognizing threat in her vast bulk, dispersed at the last second like leaves in a whirlwind. Her great jaws, meaning to put a shuddering end to one of the fleeing fish, closed instead on several chain-like weed stalks on the edge of the very elodea bed in which her quarry had found haven.

Backing out, in the same motion wheeling as though in a fretful reaction, fins and tail thrust her powerfully ahead.

Minutes later she was still trailing the weed. But sudden distaste caused her to rear and eject it.

Under her now was a tongue of rock, reaching into the lake like a sleeping serpent. Past that the water deepened. She welcomed at last a forest of ruffle-leaved pondweed. Well down in the ragged fringe she could lie undetected, shielded from the light.

Later, when she had fed, she would return to deep water. There, she always felt safest.

An hour from the time they had set out, the boys were still fishless.

"That ol' snare—it just scares 'em," Billy grumbled. Three times in the sun-glazed pools between the lily-pads they had seen fine fish. Three times Mat had extended the prop only to see the water convulse and the fish speed away.

Disgustedly, Mat thrust the prop under the seat, quite ready, himself, to give up.

"Now can I try my rod? Now. Can I?"

"Let's try the weed bed past Pinnacle Point," suggested Sam. It was a spot not far away where he often went fishing with his father. There was a tapering rock bar, where bass lurked. Beyond it was a veritable jungle of weed. "Maybe Billy will get a pickerel." Then, to strengthen the position from which Mat might otherwise retreat: "Your Dad may be out later to see how we're doing. If we haven't any fish or rabbits or anything, he might want us to come home."

"Golly, that's right."

The full truth of the argument hit Mat. More than anything else he wanted to prove they could subsist on their own efforts; he and Sam, at least. And while this wouldn't strictly be the case now that they were forced to rely on Billy's civilized equipment, the change of tactic was better than defeat.

For the second time that morning, they set out on a quest for food. This time Mat was at the oars, where he could issue instructions to Billy in the stern. Sam was in the bow.

Their spirits, quickly reviving, matched the splendour of the day. For a gathering wind had set the water dancing, and rock and trees and clouds all bore the bright, washed look that a still-pale sun bestowed. Gone were recollections of rabbit snares set with care in the cedar swamp the night before, which that morning had proved to be rabbitless; of nightlines which had produced only one lone catfish. Even their most recent failure seemed a small thing. Ahead lay new adventure.

Out beyond the same rock formation that Ma-Kee had crossed earlier, Billy set the lure adrift. It followed the boat a few feet away in frenzied, fiery movements until, as Billy released more line, it dropped back, soon disappearing under the surface.

"If anything takes it, Billy," warned Mat, "just hang on." He had earlier tightened the drag on the reel so the line wouldn't overrun and tangle. As an additional impediment to overrunning, he had engaged the ratchet, instructing Billy not to touch it. The move was hardly a customary one, for the ratchet was noisy and was meant only to be employed when the reel was not in use but was, under the circumstances, a useful stratagem.

Two miles in a northerly direction from Pinnacle Point was the village. Mat, rowing at trolling speed, could see the church spire, the tin roof of the planing mill, and Chambers' Wharf. His cottage and Sam's were in a bay on the same side of the lake as the village, and couldn't be seen from where they were. Mat thought of his parents, and wondered if they were worried about Billy. Suddenly he felt a trifle homesick.

He looked at his brother's face. Pride seemed to fairly burst from it. Then he noticed Billy's rod. It had taken a determined bend despite the fact that the reel handle was turning.

Billy, feeling the sudden pull, tried without success to grasp and hold the handle. The pressure was too great. At first pleasurably startled, he quickly showed disappointment.

"Heck!" he burst out. "I'm caught on a log. Stop rowing, Mat."

"I *have* stopped." Mat watched the unwinding reel, vainly trying to measure the turns against the speed of the still moving boat. "Are you sure it's a log?"

" 'Course I'm sure." Billy took a good grip on the rod and heaved, at the same time awkwardly pressing both thumbs against the spooled line. The rod bent again, as though he was indeed straining against some immovable object. But this time there was a difference. When he relaxed, the reel continued to turn, even though, Mat noticed, the boat, which had been travelling with the wind, was now, ever so slightly, moving the opposite way.

"You're not, Billy. I think it's a fish."

Mat's eyes scanned the water. Probably a pickerel that, having struck and run, had got the trailing hooks caught in the tough lunge weed. But he noted with a tinge of excitement that the boat was a good distance from the nearest weed tops. And the slow swell indicated deep water. Sam, speaking from experience, commented that there was nothing solid out here that a hook could catch on that he knew of.

The next moment all three boys were struck motionless within themselves, robbed of speech and action.

A few boat lengths from them, a great fish rose from the water; a fish so large as to seem unreal. A humming bird the size of a hawk, suddenly sighted, or a wriggling sheep-headed sea serpent, might have seemed no more incredible. For it did not seem possible that the familiar lake could house such a giant. But there was no mistaking the reality of the big fish now surging skyward. There was no mistaking either the police-dog head and jaws, the black-barred boa-constrictor body.

A muskie! But such a muskie!

Gracing the lobby of the village hotel was a big muskellunge of bygone days. Many times Mat had stood gazing at the stuffed specimen, oblivious of the straw innards that in several places had begun to break through; conscious only of the ugly beauty of the fish and of its great size.

Comparing the two now, Mat saw in a swift surge of awe

that this fish was larger by far. And the stuffed one was said to have been a record-breaker!

Labouring, the great fish did not quite clear the surface. For one long second it appeared to be nailed to the sky, in such a way as to keep it poised at the crescendo of its leap without interfering with its violent threshing. Then, as gravity won over muscle, it fell back. But not before the yawning mouth revealed a spot of garish colour.

Billy's lure!

Up, up and out!

Out into the thin dryness of the boat world. Out into the mysterious region where light-headedness always assailed her. Out where, except for emergencies such as this, or when the demands of appetite prevailed, she had no business to be. Out where she could shake herself free of yet another of those strange prickly beings she had so often captured and had so often found instantly distasteful.

Thus the familiar urging that had sent Ma-Kee exploding into the vision of the young fishermen.

But now she is back in her own environment, discomfited to find the prickly nuisance still with her. Its thin steely strength prompts her to run. This tactic so often brought about the defeat of these strange creatures. After a time they seemed suddenly to go lifeless, although in death they still clung to her.

Away then!

In the boat the boys hardly dared move. The line was now running out at a great rate, controlled by the braking mechanism of the reel and by such additional tension as the ratchet afforded.

Billy, instinctively obeying Mat's admonition to hang on no matter what, still had a tight grip on the cork handle of the rod. He held it in much the same way a ball player holds a bat. Thus his hands were clear of both line and reel handle:

a piece of good fortune. For, to the accompaniment of the scream of the ratchet, the reel handle was turning at a pace that suggested it had several handle grips rather than two. At length, however, his small-boy terror made itself manifest. Sight of the great fish with its large and ugly head had been provocation enough. Added to this was his sudden awareness of his personal relationship with the runaway monster.

"Mat, I'm afraid." His lips trembled and he seemed about to cry.

Jerked to his senses, Mat reached forward and took the rod from his brother. The fish was still running. If all the line ran out with Billy still holding on, there was the chance he might be pulled overboard. In his mind's eye Mat could see the gleaming spindle, the knot where the line was tied to it. Feverishly he braced himself. Another few yards now and the shock would come.

But the crisis was not reached.

Two hundred feet away Ma-Kee swirled on the surface, once more trying to shake herself free of the spiny annoyance. Back then, toward the boat, but in a wide tangent, like a dog sideways to the leash.

In turning, she had partially submitted to the resisting force of the line. Now the strange power of the creature she had seized is seemingly dissipated, and she feels unimpeded. It is still there in her jaw, however; still able to maintain its hold; still able to retaliate with stinging hurts. And so it must be got rid of, or swallowed. She does not know, at the moment, which would give her greater satisfaction.

Her sidelong run brings the broad belly of the boat within Ma-Kee's view. Instantly she turns away from it, conscious of a deep-seated mistrust of its presence. Off again now, in accelerated flight. But hold: what odd happening is this? The maddening pressure on her snout, so recently relieved, is back again.

Ma-Kee herself has picked up the slack caused by her about-face and is once more fighting a tight line. But, of course, the old muskie cannot know. She merely finds this new turn of events exasperating. Well, she will set matters to rights quickly enough!

By now, Sam had crept to the oars. Mat was in the stern seat, Billy on the floor between them. Physically better adjusted, they had had time also to adjust mentally to the situation.

"What a lunker!" Sam breathed. "It must be that monster muskie I've heard Pop talk about. Everybody's been trying to catch it. And imagine, Billy, here, hooked it!" He winked at Billy. Then, with a coolness he did not feel, he said to Mat, "Wouldn't it be something if we could land it?"

Mat, finding the big fish still on despite the long interval when the line was slack, felt a strange exhilaration at the words . . . *if we could land it!*

A few moments before, while he would not have admitted it, he had had a wild desire to abandon the rod, to cut the line: anything to be rid of the big fish. It was an unsought adventure; a secret of the lake they had not meant to uncover; a threat that hung over them like the genie released from Aladdin's lamp.

Just to have seen the monster fish was a frightening thing. To know they were chained to it was a great deal more so. He knew if he kept thinking that way he would get that scared feeling all over again. But Sam—good old Sam—had snapped him out of it.

. . . *if we could land it!*

Time was on their side. The hour was just past noon. They could fight the muskie the rest of the day if they had to. Mat had two chocolate bars in his pocket. Small pieces, slipped into their mouths every so often, would stave off their hunger.

The wind, too, was in their favour. In strength it was hardly more than could be called a wind. And it was blowing from the south, straight down the lake, inclining to drift the boat away from the weedy, log-strewn shore waters while still not threatening to carry them far out into the wider expanse of lake to the east.

As for the big muskie, they could only hope for the same luck they had had so far. The first big leap of a muskie, they knew, was the crucial test. If the line held, if the fish did not shake the lure, there was a good chance it would not be lost in the ensuing battle. There could be trouble at the finish, though. A muskie could be the very devil to land—particularly if it was a big one. Unlike a pike, it never seemed to lose its strength. The touch of a net or a hand, just when capture was imminent, would often trigger a violent display of energy and send the fish rocketing away as though the fight had just begun, perhaps leaving behind a broken rod or line, and a thoroughly chagrined angler.

All three of them lifting, Mat knew, could never get this fish into the boat, even if it was completely exhausted; even, indeed, if they had net or gaff, of which they had neither.

But that was another matter. Their prize victim was still on; that was the main thing. First, it had to be subdued. There was time enough to think about what to do after that.

Twice Ma-Kee circled the boat in a wide arc with Mat keeping just enough tension on the line to maintain control. He was not concerned now about the fish making another run. Twice it had taken out two hundred feet or so of line. It was predictable that the big fish would not again make a run of such length.

Then began a series of bulldogging sorties, always at a sharp downward angle. But the more Ma-Kee sought to punish the spiny thing in her jaw the more it bit into her, or pierced her with its spines, she did not know which.

Savagely, twenty feet down, she shook her head. Still her tormentor clung heavily to her. So it was not yet to be mastered. Well, up then!

She did not charge up, but came gradually. The move imparted to Mat the suspicion, before long confirmed, that the big muskie was going to try another leap.

On sudden impulse he dug the rod tip into the water, thinking to discourage the leap by snubbing the big fish. It was a trick, he knew, that was often used by muskie fishermen. And because of the strength of the line and the considerable distance between boat and fish, the ruse worked: at least, seemed to. A hundred feet out Ma-Kee surfaced. But only her head emerged. And when at length she had had enough of head-shaking and started again the slow trip down into deep water, Sam took in a deep breath and gazed admiringly at his friend.

"Bully for you, Mat. That stopped him. Boy! What Pop wouldn't give to see us now."

Mat grinned, a feeling of faintness suddenly leaving him. "My Dad, too. Bet they'd both do back flips."

An hour passed, during which time Sam took the rod, and Mat and Billy looked on anxiously. Actually, it had been an uneventful sixty minutes. Far down in her water world Ma-Kee sulks, moving but fitfully. She is puzzled by the whole affair; not inclined for the moment to resume the fight, for some of her great strength is gone; yet not inclined either to give way to the steady pressure of the line. The gloom of the deep water comforts her. For there the mystery is not compounded by sight of the ever-present boat which she connects in some devious way with her predicament. There the greater oxygen content of the water is an aid to her laboured breathing. There too she can nurse her wounds of spirit.

Another interval now when once again Mat takes over the rod. It seems almost a signal for Ma-Kee to be on the move.

So much line is out that Mat dares not risk giving more. The result is that Ma-Kee tows the boat, taking them some distance off course. But the effort soon tires her and she is glad to stop and rest. There is a limit even to her powers of endurance.

Rowing back on course again, the boys find that the big fish follows willingly. But they know it is not to be trusted, even now; and so, as best they can, they keep a close watch on its every move.

"Golly, I wish a boat would come," murmured Billy. For him the adventure had lost some of its glamour.

"There will be, Billy. Don't worry."

But they were some distance from the boat lanes and Mat knew it. When they did see a boat half an hour later it was so far away that their waving brought no more than the customary answering salute.

If they were to get help, it was plain, it would be from some passing fisherman.

How long had they been fighting the big fish? Mat, looking at his watch, estimated three hours, then found to his dismay that the watch had stopped.

"Seems more like a year to me," said Sam.

Ma-Kee's runs now are infrequent, and almost always on a short line. Once, she swam not an oar's length under the boat. Her nightmare form, seen amid the cloud reflections, made the water appear as sky and the fish some grotesque and unwieldy kite soaring above.

Desperately, at last, she sounds. There, on the bottom, she remains for so long a time that the boys, with sinking hearts, fancy she has escaped, leaving them hooked on a log or rock in her stead. But the steady pressure of the line at length summons her up out of the friendly depths.

She is fast losing her equilibrium. When, slowly, she surfaces, like a spent torpedo, her ponderous form lists. For a long moment she lies on her side, an awe-inspiring spectacle, before weaving a tortuous way down out of sight.

"We're winning!" Sam shouts exultantly. "It's giving up!"

It was true.

The old muskellunge, chained to the boat by the slenderest of tethers, was at last fighting a losing battle. Her great strength, the strength of jaw and fin and tail that had brought her successfully through many a harsh test, was ebbing. A feeling of lightness comes over her. Her fins refuse to maintain her downward progress. Once more her head lifts and she rises into the glare of the boat world.

What is she doing there? The coontail forests summon her:

the murky depths of the ship channel, where she can be relieved of these strange happenings. Dimly she is aware of the boat, which Sam is intent on keeping a safe distance from the weeds. It has its oars in the water and is swimming away from her. She must rush after it and swallow it or it will get away.

But instead she is led along ignominiously, her fins propelling her blindly in the boat's wake.

"Listen!" says Mat suddenly. "A boat! I'll bet it's Charlie Wheeler. He generally fishes the Reach on Wednesday. It's his day off."

The boat, powered by a 25-horsepower outboard, quickly drew down on them. At first slowing so as not to endanger them with his wake, then cutting the motor when he was fifty feet from their starboard, Charlie Wheeler, the village Postmaster, leaned on the gearshift and tucked his chaw into the far cheek. He was a thin man with a big jaw and a walrus moustache dyed deep tobacco brown along its lower extremities.

"What are you kids doing out here?" he demanded. "It's near six o'clock, Mat. You should be in for supper."

Billy was the first to find words.

"We've got a muskie on—a big one, a really awful big one. An' we got him on my new rod."

"Come again," drawled Charlie, preparing to spit.

"It's true—don't come too close!" warned Mat. "Look!" And he pointed behind the boat where Ma-Kee trailed like a log that had got free of a boom. "But we don't know how to land him."

Instead of spitting, the Postmaster swallowed. Words that wanted to come would have been fitting to the occasion but unsuited to tender ears. It was a moment or two before he was able, vocally, to express his reaction to what he saw.

"Holy goshall mackerel!" he choked. "Is it ever a muskie! It's as big as a house."

A man of action, he wasted no time with further words.

"You kids wait here!" he commanded. "Don't do anything.

But hang onto that fish. It's only a five-minute run to the village and I'll be back before you know it. We need the biggest gol-darned muskie net ever invented."

Actually, Charlie Wheeler made it in four minutes. In another minute he paused breathlessly at the railway station.

Keep that wire open!" he instructed the telegraph operator with a voice of authority. "And call the *Dispatch* to get somebody over here fast. Some kids from the Bay have got that monster muskie on up below Pinnacle Point. If they land it, it'll be the story of the year."

The rest of Charlie Wheeler's mad dash is history. When he started back down the lake six minutes later, he had the biggest muskie net in all the village. And a dozen boats followed in his wake.

Reaching the boys and finding they still had the giant muskie in tow, Charlie Wheeler's first job was to see that all the boats kept their distance.

"If one of them cuts that line," he seethed, "I'll . . ."

With a megaphone, contributed by the sports store, he marshalled the flotilla. By this time binoculars were in hand and excited onlookers one by one announced that "There's no fooling. It's just the way Charlie Wheeler said. True, you can't see the big fish very well—only its back and tail. But——"

Manoeuvring around beside the boat where Billy, Mat and Sam were now the centre of attraction, the Postmaster passed the long-handled net to Sam. If Mat could get the fish up near where the two boats came together, he and Sam could both have a go at it.

But when the Postmaster saw Ma-Kee at close hand, he knew it was no use. There was never a net made that would handle that fish!

And that is when Mat hit on his idea. In the boat, under the seats where he had thrust it, was the fish snare. If he could get it around the fish and yank it tight, they had a good chance to beach the big muskie without getting it fouled in weeds or unseen obstructions.

Mat himself managed the trick. A false try first, that caused Ma-Kee to shoot forward in dull alarm and triggered sharp intakes of breath by those who could see. Then a second, this one successful. Down and over the tail he passed the enlarged noose, drawing it ever so carefully toward him. When it was just back of the enormous gill covers, he gave a sharp jerk— and Ma-Kee was lassoed.

On a nearby point they dragged her ashore, far enough up so that there was little danger of her ever escaping. Even at that, they felt it necessary to try to keep her in one spot; for what little strength she had left was magnified a dozen-fold in the thin air. The Postmaster, bearing down on the prop like a lumberman pinning a log with his peavy in choppy water, still was seesawed with each heave of her great body. Others tried to imprison her tail. But none dared touch her head.

It was a fitting finale for so great a fish. And when at length it was all over and she grew still, the noose was removed and they crowded close around her.

She lay there resplendent in the early evening light : a sight few had ever thought to see. Some, noting the splendid lines of her body, the soft infusion of red in her tail, the silvery expanse of scale and the golden almost-subterranean glow in the one eye exposed to their view, thought her magnificent. Others, touching hesitant fingers to the mucilaginous coating of her body or making wry faces at the coppery blotches on her flanks—a sign of her great age—thought her repulsive.

It remained for those who looked closely at her head and jaws in all their ugly reality to make the most quotable observation : "A regular dragon," they summed up.

The disfigurement left by Krark's beak, the scars of other encounters, all were there, all were exclaimed on. And what turned out to be a tag was found buried in one huge opercle. Miraculously, the small plastic disc had remained, sewn so firmly in her gill plate that it was partly grown over with osseous tissue. Providing it could be read, it would enable the biologists to trace her history so faithfully that none could doubt.

Later, back at the village, while the telegraph operator excitedly waited to tap out the message that would send news of the catch circulating throughout the country, Ma-Kee was suspended like a side of beef from the scales at the freight yard. Seventy-eight pounds! From snout to tail tip she was found to measure four inches better than five feet. Her girth (Billy could no more than get his arms around her) was almost thirty-seven inches. Surely never was such a muskie seen before.

To the boys went the newspaper award. Their pictures appeared in the papers wherever fishing was news, which was practically everywhere; their story was told again and again. . . .

But, after all, it was not their story. It was the story of a great fish : the great muskellunge of the Kawarthas; a story that, for the most part, none would ever know.

Little Tom heard. In due course, when Ma-Kee was suitably mounted and propped in the window of the newspaper office, he went and stood on the fringe of the crowd and gazed upon her. And although he felt sorrow, he felt a gladness, too.

The great *kinonge* was gone. But it would live on, in spirit.

Perhaps her spirit would take another form. He would look for it in the mists that gathered on the lake at dawn. He would listen for it on the night wind.